Key Accounting Principles Volume I

An Introductory Financial Accounting Course

Workbook

Neville Joffe

AME | Learning

ISBN: 978-1-926751-10-8

Key Accounting Principles Volume I - Workbook
Author: Neville Joffe
Publisher: AME Learning
Developmental Editor: Graeme Gomes
Production Editor: Miresh Puradchithasan
Content Reviewer: Guy Groisman
Typesetter: Paragon Prepress Inc.
Project Manager: Linda Zhang
Cover Design: Edward Phung
Online Course Design & Production: AME Multimedia Team

For more information contact:

AME Learning Inc.
303-1200 Sheppard Avenue East
Toronto, ON, Canada M2K 2S5
Phone: 416.848.4399
Toll-free: 1.888.401.3881
E-mail: info@amelearning.com
Visit our website at: www.amelearning.com

Table of Contents

Chapter 1

PERSONAL ACCOUNTING

Assessment Questions

AS-1 (❶)

Define accounting and state the purpose of accounting.

AS-2 (❶)

What is net worth?

AS-3 (❷)

In simple terms, what are assets and liabilities?

AS-4 (❷)

What are revenues and expenses?

AS-5 (❷)

Explain the role of the balance sheet.

AS-6 (❷)

Explain the role of the income statement.

AS-7 (❷)

What are some advantages of using monthly accounting periods in your personal balance sheet?

AS-8 (❸)

What is the accounting equation?

AS-9 (❶)

What is the equation for calculating closing net worth for a period?

AS-10 (❷)

Define surplus (and deficit).

AS-11 (❹)

What is a T-Account?

AS-12 (❺)

Define the principle of accrual accounting.

AS-13 (❺)

Briefly describe the cash-based method of accounting.

AS-14 (❻)

Explain the matching principle.

AS-15 (❶)

True or False: When you borrow money, you have more cash but your net worth decreases.

____

AS-16 (❶)

True or False: When you pay off a loan, your cash decreases and your net worth increases.

____

____

AS-17 (❶)

True or False: Buying an asset has no impact on net worth.

____

AS-18 (❼)

Describe the concept of depreciation.

____

____

____

____

AS-19 (❺)

What is a prepaid expense?

____

____

AS-20 (❺)

When an expense is initially prepaid, which accounts increase or decrease?

____

____

AS-21 (❻)

What are the three ways to recognize an expense?

AS-22 (❻)

Describe the concept of materiality in the context of assets and expenses.

AS-23 (❽)

What is capital?

AS-24 (❿)

Define market value.

AS-25 (❿)

Define book value.

Application Questions

AP-1 (❶)

Darryl purchased a new laptop on January 1, 2010 worth $2,000. He paid the entire amount ($2,000) using cash. He also purchased a new cell phone worth $300 and an mp3 player worth $100, on account. How will these transactions affect Darryl's net worth?

AP-2 (❷)

April Rose had the following financial data for the year ended December 31, 2012:

Cash	$6,000
Jewelry	10,000
Automobile	18,000
House	56,000
Bank Loan	45,000
Credit Card	5,000
Mortgage Payable	40,000

Required:

a) Calculate April Rose's total assets.

b) Calculate April Rose's total liabilities.

AP-3 (➊, ➋)

Consider the following information of Julius Troy:

Cash	$12,000
Jewelry	18,000
Automobile	22,000
House	61,000
Credit Card	5,000
Bank Loan	10,000
Mortgage Payable	25,000

Required:

a) Calculate Julius Troy's total assets.

b) Calculate Julius Troy's total liabilities.

c) Calculate Julius Troy's net worth.

AP-4 (❶, ❸)

Consider the following information:

Cash	$6,000
Automobile	50,000
Prepaid Insurance	3,000
Mortgage Payable	10,000
Unpaid Credit Card Bills	2,000
Net Worth	?

How much is the net worth?

AP-5 (❷, ❸)

A worker has the following information with regards to his own balance sheet, but the liability section is missing.

Cash	$35,000
Automobile	58,000
House	100,000
Net Worth	55,000

Required: Determine the amount of liability.

AP-6 (❶, ❷, ❹)

Following information was taken from the personal records of Juliet Lahm:

Opening Balances:	
Cash	$3,000
Jewelry	2,000
House	90,000
Mortgage Payable	80,000
Net Worth	15,000

The following are the transactions for the month of May 2011:

1.	Received monthly salary	$5,000
2.	Paid cash for utilities	1,200
3.	Purchased an automobile on account	10,000
4.	Paid cash for food expenses	600
5.	Received interest earned on bank deposits	50
6.	Paid cash for gas	400

a) What is the ending balance of cash?

INCREASE (DR) +	CASH	DECREASE (CR) -
Opening Bal.		

b) What is the surplus or deficit for the period?

Personal Income Statement For the Month Ended May 31, 2011	

c) What is Juliet Lahm's net worth on May 31?

____

____

____

____

AP-7 (❶, ❸)

As of December 31, 2010, Maria Green had total assets of $40,000, and total liabilities of $15,000. As of December 31, 2011, Maria's total assets and liabilities increased to $50,000 and $30,000, respectively. How has Maria's net worth changed since the end of 2010?

____

____

____

____

AP-8 (❶, ❷, ❸, ❹)

The following information pertains to Ken White's personal financial transactions :

Opening Balances at January 1, 2011	
Cash	$9,000
House	56,000
Automobile	29,000
Contents of Home	6,000
Unpaid Accounts	5,500
Bank Loan	60,000
Net Worth	34,500

The following are the transactions for the month of January 2011:

1.	Paid maintenance expense for the month of January with cash	$120
2.	Sold furniture for cash (assume the furniture is sold at the balance sheet value)	2,000
3.	Purchased new furniture as a replacement for the old one, using cash	2,500

4.	Paid credit card liability in full	5,500
5.	Paid telephone, electricity and water bill for January with cash	1,200
6.	Purchased groceries and goods for personal consumption with cash	2,000
7.	Deposited salary earned during the month	4,000
8.	Earned interest on savings account	40

Required:

a) Using the information provided, record the opening balances in the T-accounts.

b) Record the transactions for the month of January in the T-accounts.

c) Complete the personal balance sheet and income statement.

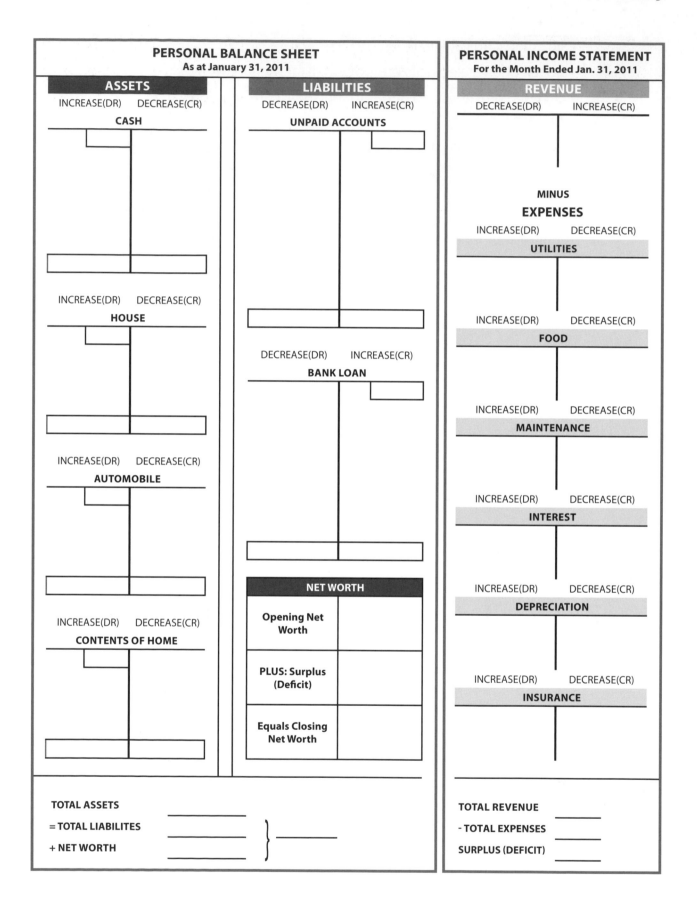

PERSONAL BALANCE SHEET
As at January 31, 2011

ASSETS

INCREASE(DR) DECREASE(CR)
CASH

INCREASE(DR) DECREASE(CR)
HOUSE

INCREASE(DR) DECREASE(CR)
AUTOMOBILE

INCREASE(DR) DECREASE(CR)
CONTENTS OF HOME

LIABILITIES

DECREASE(DR) INCREASE(CR)
UNPAID ACCOUNTS

DECREASE(DR) INCREASE(CR)
BANK LOAN

NET WORTH

Opening Net Worth	
PLUS: Surplus (Deficit)	
Equals Closing Net Worth	

TOTAL ASSETS ________
= TOTAL LIABILITES ________
+ NET WORTH ________

PERSONAL INCOME STATEMENT
For the Month Ended Jan. 31, 2011

REVENUE

DECREASE(DR) INCREASE(CR)

MINUS

EXPENSES

INCREASE(DR) DECREASE(CR)
UTILITIES

INCREASE(DR) DECREASE(CR)
FOOD

INCREASE(DR) DECREASE(CR)
MAINTENANCE

INCREASE(DR) DECREASE(CR)
INTEREST

INCREASE(DR) DECREASE(CR)
DEPRECIATION

INCREASE(DR) DECREASE(CR)
INSURANCE

TOTAL REVENUE ________
- TOTAL EXPENSES ________
SURPLUS (DEFICIT) ________

KEN WHITE PERSONAL BALANCE SHEET AS AT JANUARY 31, 2011	

KEN WHITE PERSONAL INCOME STATEMENT FOR THE MONTH ENDED JANUARY 31, 2011	

AP-9 (❶, ❷, ❸, ❹)

Alan Marshall is preparing his balance sheet and income statement for the month ended April 30, 2011. Use the following information to help him prepare his financial statements.

Opening Balances - April 1, 2011	
Cash	$5,000
Contents of Home	1,000
Automobile	4,000
House	80,000
Unpaid Accounts	10,000
Auto Loan	30,000
Net Worth	50,000

The following are the transactions for the month of April:

1.	Purchased new furniture for home using the credit card	$2,000
2.	Paid credit card bill with cash	3,000
3.	Paid utility bills for the month of April using the credit card	800
4.	Purchased groceries and food using cash	2,500
5.	Made the annual principal payment for the auto loan	1,250
6.	Paid the April's rent with cash	1,500
7.	Deposited salaries earned during the month	4,000
8.	Earned interest on savings account	50

Required:

a) Using the information provided, record the opening balances in the T-accounts.

b) Record the transactions for the month of April in the T-accounts.

c) Complete the personal balance sheet and income statement.

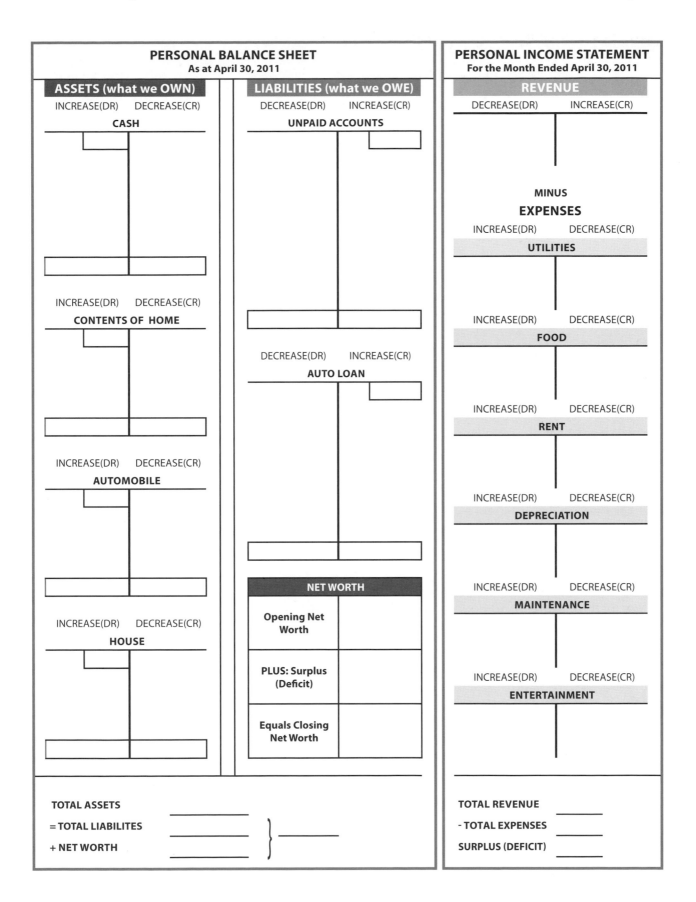

PERSONAL BALANCE SHEET
As at April 30, 2011

ASSETS (what we OWN)

INCREASE(DR) DECREASE(CR)
CASH

INCREASE(DR) DECREASE(CR)
CONTENTS OF HOME

INCREASE(DR) DECREASE(CR)
AUTOMOBILE

INCREASE(DR) DECREASE(CR)
HOUSE

LIABILITIES (what we OWE)

DECREASE(DR) INCREASE(CR)
UNPAID ACCOUNTS

DECREASE(DR) INCREASE(CR)
AUTO LOAN

NET WORTH	
Opening Net Worth	
PLUS: Surplus (Deficit)	
Equals Closing Net Worth	

TOTAL ASSETS ______
= TOTAL LIABILITES ______
+ NET WORTH ______ } ______

PERSONAL INCOME STATEMENT
For the Month Ended April 30, 2011

REVENUE

DECREASE(DR) INCREASE(CR)

MINUS

EXPENSES

INCREASE(DR) DECREASE(CR)
UTILITIES

INCREASE(DR) DECREASE(CR)
FOOD

INCREASE(DR) DECREASE(CR)
RENT

INCREASE(DR) DECREASE(CR)
DEPRECIATION

INCREASE(DR) DECREASE(CR)
MAINTENANCE

INCREASE(DR) DECREASE(CR)
ENTERTAINMENT

TOTAL REVENUE ______
- TOTAL EXPENSES ______
SURPLUS (DEFICIT) ______

ALAN MARSHALL PERSONAL BALANCE SHEET AS AT APRIL 30, 2011	

ALAN MARSHALL PERSONAL INCOME STATEMENT FOR THE MONTH ENDED APRIL 30, 2011	

AP-10 (❶, ❷)

John Black is a senior administrator at a market research firm, and has recently experienced a salary increase from $3,500 per month to $4,000 per month. He feels richer and would like to know the increase in his net worth. However, he has never prepared a personal balance sheet or an income statement that would help him understand his net worth. The following information has been gathered by John in an attempt to better understand his financial position.

	September 30, 2010	October 31, 2010	November 30, 2010
Cash	$1,000	$2,150	$4,050
House	120,000	120,000	120,000
Bank Loan	400	350	300
Salary	3,500	3,500	4,000
Entertainment Expense	200	500	400
Food Expense	1,500	1,200	1,100
Insurance Expense	150	150	150
Utilities Expense	200	400	300
Miscellaneous Expense	175	50	100

Required: Prepare John Black's income statement and balance sheet for the three months.

John Black Personal Income Statement For the Month				
	September	October	November	Total

John Black Balance Sheet As at Month End			
	September	October	November

AP-11 (❶, ❷)

Ethan is a famous songwriter and composer. His income is based solely on royalties that he receives regularly. Ethan opted to use three months as his accounting period.

The following information pertains to income earned and expenses incurred from January 1, 2011 to March 31, 2011

	January	February	March
Royalty Income	$12,000	$13,000	$10,000
Interest Expense	60	60	60
Food Expense	2,000	2,100	1,900
Maintenance Expense	350	500	180
Clothing Expense	900	1,500	0
Utilities Expense	300	500	0
Rent Expense	1,500	1,500	1,500
Miscellaneous Expense	15	50	5

Required:

a) Prepare a personal income statement for each of the three months.

Ethan Personal Income Statement For the Period Ended March 31, 2011				
	January	February	March	Total

b) What amount should be added to Ethan's net worth on March 31, 2011.

AP-12 (❸)

Calculate the missing amounts in the following table.

	Scenario 1	Scenario 2
Total Assets	$123,000	
Total Liabilities		$34,000
Net Worth	$94,000	$114,000

AP-13 (❷)

Using the opening balances provided in the balance sheets below, enter the updated amounts for each transaction in the blank balance sheets marked "Answers".

1. Borrowed $4,000 from the bank.

Opening Balances

Assets		**Liabilities**	
Cash	5,000	Bank Loan	0
House	80,000	Unpaid Accounts	3,000
Automobile	20,000	Mortgage Payable	50,000
Contents of Home	6,000	Automobile Loan	5,000
Investment	8,000	Student Loan	6,000
		Total Liabilities	64,000
		Net Worth	55,000
Total Assets	**119,000**	**Liabilities + Net Worth**	**119,000**

Answers:

Assets		**Liabilities**	
Cash		Bank Loan	
House		Unpaid Accounts	
Automobile		Mortgage Payable	
Contents of Home		Automobile Loan	
Investment		Student Loan	
		Total Liabilities	
		Net Worth	
Total Assets		**Liabilities + Net Worth**	

2. Sold investments for $8,000 cash.

Opening Balances

Assets		**Liabilities**	
Cash	1,000	Bank Loan	0
House	80,000	Unpaid Accounts	3,000
Automobile	20,000	Mortgage Payable	50,000
Contents of Home	6,000	Automobile Loan	5,000
Investment	8,000	Student Loan	6,000
		Total Liabilities	**64,000**
		Net Worth	51,000
Total Assets	**115,000**	**Liabilities + Net Worth**	**115,000**

Answers:

Assets		**Liabilities**	
Cash		Bank Loan	
House		Unpaid Accounts	
Automobile		Mortgage Payable	
Contents of Home		Automobile Loan	
Investment		Student Loan	
		Total Liabilities	
		Net Worth	
Total Assets		**Liabilities + Net Worth**	

3. Paid $1,000 to reduce an outstanding automobile loan (principal portion).

Opening Balances

Assets		**Liabilities**	
Cash	3,000	Bank Loan	0
House	80,000	Unpaid Accounts	3,000
Automobile	20,000	Mortgage Payable	50,000
Contents of Home	6,000	Automobile Loan	5,000
		Student Loan	6,000
		Total Liabilities	**64,000**
		Net Worth	45,000
Total Assets	**109,000**	**Liabilities + Net Worth**	**109,000**

Answers:

Assets		**Liabilities**	
Cash		Bank Loan	
House		Unpaid Accounts	
Automobile		Mortgage Payable	
Contents of Home		Automobile Loan	
		Student Loan	
		Total Liabilities	
		Net Worth	
Total Assets		**Liabilities + Net Worth**	

4. Bought a motorcycle for $6,000 - paid a $1,000 deposit with cash and borrowed $5,000 from the bank.

Opening Balances

Assets		**Liabilities**	
Cash	2,000	Bank Loan	1,000
House	80,000	Unpaid Accounts	3,000
Automobile	20,000	Mortgage Payable	50,000
Contents of Home	4,000	Automobile Loan	5,000
Motorcycle	-	Student Loan	6,000
		Total Liabilities	**65,000**
		Net Worth	41,000
Total Assets	**106,000**	**Liabilities + Net Worth**	**106,000**

Answers:

Assets		**Liabilities**	
Cash		Bank Loan	
House		Unpaid Accounts	
Automobile		Mortgage Payable	
Contents of Home		Automobile Loan	
Motorcycle		Student Loan	
		Total Liabilities	
		Net Worth	
Total Assets		**Liabilities + Net Worth**	

AP-14 (❷)

Using the following chart, indicate whether there would be an increase, decrease or no change to the bank balance and net worth for the transactions provided. *The first transaction has been completed for you.*

		Bank Balance			**Net Worth**		
	Transaction	**Increase**	**Decrease**	**No Change**	**Increase**	**Decrease**	**No Change**
1	Deposit salary	X			X		
2	Pay cash for food						
3	Take a loan to buy a new car						
4	Sell a stereo for cash						
5	Reduce student loan principal						
6	Buy a new computer for cash						
7	Deposit a bank loan						
8	Pay entertainment expenses						
9	Record interest received on savings						

AP-15 (❶, ❸)

State how the following transactions would impact net worth (increase, decrease, no change):

Item	**Effect on Net Worth**
Borrow cash	
Pay entertainment expense with cash	
Pay food expense with cash	
Buy assets with cash	
Charge home repairs expense on credit card	
Pay insurance expense with cash	
Pay loan principal with cash	
Purchase assets on account	
Receive salary	
Pay rent expense with cash	

AP-16 (❶, ❷, ❸, ❻)

On December 1, 2010, Shervin decided to track his finances. On this date, his assets and liabilities were as follows:

Cash	$14,000
Prepaid Rent	3,000
Prepaid Insurance	300
House	60,000
Contents of Home	19,000
Automobile	30,000
Student Loan	10,000
Unpaid Accounts	17,000
Bank Loan	25,000
Mortgage Payable	25,000

a) What is the value of his total assets?

b) What is the value of his total liabilities?

c) What is Shervin's net worth on December 1, 2010?

d) During the month of December, Shervin recognized $150 of prepaid expenses as an actual expense on the income statement.
Calculate the change in his cash account and personal net worth.

Transaction	Cash	Net Worth
Effect		

AP-17 (❸, ❺, ❻)

Arthur's financial records show that his assets and net worth as of May 1, 2010 are as follows:

Cash	$6,000
Computer	4,000
Automobile	20,000
House	37,500
Contents of Home	17,500
Student Loan	?
Net Worth	13,000

a) Arthur wants to find out how much he owes. Determine his total liabilities.

b) During the month of May, Arthur paid $2,000 for two months of rent in advance ($1,000 per month). Calculate the change in Arthur's cash account and personal net worth.

Transaction	Cash	Net Worth
Effect		

AP-18 (❻)

Peter's total net worth is $235,000. Use the materiality principle to help classify each of the following as an asset or an expense.

Item	Amount	Expense/Asset
CD	$15	
House	100,000	
Laptop	2,000	
Food	80	
Gas for Automobile	30	
Concert Tickets	250	
Furniture	3,000	

AP-19 (❼)

On January 1, 2011, Tristan purchased a brand new car and a cell phone worth $45,000 and $1,200 respectively. It is estimated that the useful life of the car is 9 years while the cell phone has a useful life of 4 years. The depreciation is to be equally distributed each year. Calculate the depreciation expense for the first year.

AP-20 (❼)

The market value of some of Jessica's personal assets on January 1, 2010 are listed below:

Automobile	$11,000
Computer	$1,200

The automobile and computer were newly purchased on January 1, 2010. The automobile has a useful life of 10 years and the computer has a useful life of 3 years. Calculate the annual depreciation and the value of the automobile and computer on the balance sheet at year-end.

AP-21 (❽)

John Hollister collected the following amounts in cash for the month of February 2011:

Salary paid by employer	$2,400
Winnings at the casino	$270
Gifts	$220
Performance bonus paid by employer	$450

Required: Calculate John's total revenue and total capital items for February 2011.

AP-22 (❽)

Joana Harwin collected the following amounts in cash for the month of March 2011:

Interest earned on savings account	$75
Full-time employment income	$1,200
Income from part-time babysitting job	$220
Rental income	$525

Required: Calculate Joana's total revenue and total capital items for March 2011.

AP-23 (❾)

Yelena Rollins incurred the following transactions related to cash for the month of May 2011:

- Invested in property
- Borrowed a bank loan
- Paid back a portion of a student loan
- Paid telephone bill
- Earned a salary from a part-time job

Of the three sources and uses of cash, how many ways did Yelena increase or decrease cash for May? Classify each of the above transactions according to the three sources and uses of cash.

Case Study

CS – 1 (❶, ❷, ❸, ❹)

After taking the first part of this financial accounting course, you excitedly tell a friend of yours what you have learned. You tell him about assets, liabilities and net worth and how they increase and decrease in value with every financial transaction. Your friend decides to start getting organized and apply accounting principles to his personal finance. He compiles everything that he thinks is important and calculates his net worth. He then asks you to look over what he had done to make sure it is correct. His list of important financial items is listed below, along with his version of the T-Account records.

1	He had $950 in his bank account at the beginning of the month.
2	He had a $1,200 balance on his credit card at the beginning of the month.
3	He estimates that he had about $3,000 worth of "stuff" in his apartment at the beginning of the month (TV, sound system, computer and furniture).
4	Deposited his salary of $1,500.
5	Paid in advance for three months of rent with $1,350 cash.
6	Paid $600 to pay off a portion of the credit card bill.
7	Purchased a new video game system for $350 with his credit card.
8	Bought $120 worth of food with cash.
9	Got hired at a second job. He will start next month and will earn $800 per month.
10	Spent $250 cash on movies, stage plays and Dave and Buster's.
11	Lived in his apartment for one of the three months he already paid for (see #5)

+	Cash		-
1	$950	5	$1,350
4	$1,500	6	$600
		8	$120
		10	$250
Total	$130		

-	Unpaid Accounts		+
6	$600	2	$1,200
		7	$350
		Total	$950

-	Net Worth		+
5	$1,350	3	$3,000
8	$120	4	$1,500
10	$250	7	$350
		9	$800
		Total	$3,930

Required:

1. What are some immediate problems that you see with what your friend has prepared?

2. With all the problems you see, your friend asks you to show him what the correct records should look like. Use the provided templates located at the end of this problem to record the transactions.

After showing your friend the corrected version, he starts asking you a number of questions.

3. Why did you use all of these accounts when I only used three (Cash, Unpaid Accounts and Net Worth)?

4. Why is the $3,000 worth of "stuff" not considered net worth?

5. I was having trouble figuring out how to record my second job which I start next month. They are going to be paying me $800 a month! I figured it will increase my net worth, but I didn't know where else to put it. I knew it couldn't be cash, because they haven't paid me yet. What did you do with it and why?

6. What did you do with my rent? Shouldn't the entire $1,350 decrease my net worth? And what would happen if I did it my way?

7. I forgot to tell you that the $600 credit card payment included $30 of interest. I didn't think it mattered since the total payment amount is the same. This won't change anything, right?

8. You may have noticed that I am running low on cash. Any suggestions on how I can legally raise more cash?

9. This is very useful and I would like to do this more often. I think I can do it this weekend, then two weeks from now once I finish with my exams, then probably not for another month after that. I'm going on a well-deserved vacation after my exams, so I won't be around to look after it. Do you think this will work out well?

PERSONAL BALANCE SHEET

Assets

INCREASE (DR)	DECREASE (CR)
Opening:	
Ending	

INCREASE (DR)	DECREASE (CR)
Opening:	
Ending	

INCREASE (DR)	DECREASE (CR)
Opening:	
Ending	

Liabilities

DECREASE (DR)	INCREASE (CR)
	Opening:
	Ending

DECREASE (DR)	INCREASE (CR)
	Opening:
	Ending

NET WORTH	
Opening Net Worth	
Add: Capital	
Add: Surplus (Deficit)	
Equals Closing Net Worth	

Total Assets	
= Total Liabilities	
+ Net Worth	

PERSONAL INCOME STATEMENT

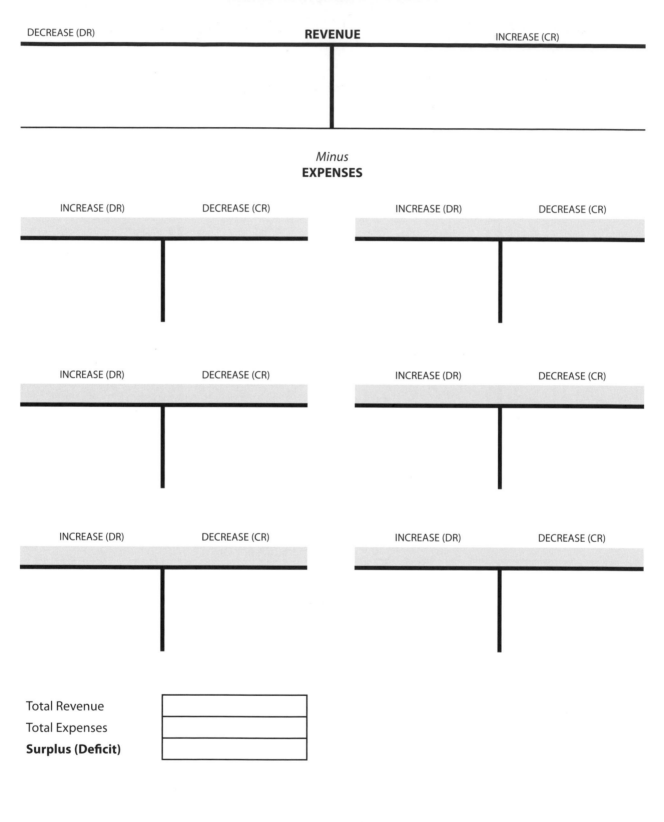

DECREASE (DR)	REVENUE	INCREASE (CR)

Minus

EXPENSES

INCREASE (DR)	DECREASE (CR)

INCREASE (DR)	DECREASE (CR)

INCREASE (DR)	DECREASE (CR)

INCREASE (DR)	DECREASE (CR)

INCREASE (DR)	DECREASE (CR)

INCREASE (DR)	DECREASE (CR)

Total Revenue	
Total Expenses	
Surplus (Deficit)	

Chapter 2

LINKING PERSONAL ACCOUNTING TO BUSINESS ACCOUNTING

Assessment Questions

AS-1 (❶)

Net worth in personal accounting is similar to which item in accounting for businesses?

AS-2 (❷)

In what order are the assets of a business listed? Explain.

AS-3 (❷)

In what order are the liabilities of a business listed? Explain.

AS-4 (❸)

What is owner's equity?

AS-5 (❸)

What is the formula for calculating the ending owner's equity balance (or ending capital account balance)?

____

____

AS-6 (❸)

Describe owner's contributions and owner's drawings and explain how they affect the balance sheet.

____

____

____

AS-7 (❹)

What is a sole proprietorship?

____

____

AS-8 (❹)

Explain unlimited liability.

____

____

____

AS-9 (❹)

What is a partnership?

____

____

AS-10 (❹)

What are the three types of partnerships that can be created?

AS-11 (❹)

What is the difference between a general partnership and a limited partnership?

AS-12 (❹)

What is a cooperative?

AS-13 (❹)

Describe a corporation.

AS-14 (❹)

What is a not-for-profit organization?

AS-15 (❹)

Provide three examples of not-for-profit organizations.

AS-16 (❺)

Define internal and external stakeholders.

AS-17 (❻)

List the three main types of businesses.

AS-18 (❻)

Explain what a service business does. Provide two examples of service businesses.

AS-19 (❻)

Explain what a merchandising business does. Provide an example of a merchandising business.

AS-20 (❻)

Explain what a manufacturing business does. Provide two examples of a manufacturing business.

AS-21 (❼)

Give three examples of expenses that businesses commonly prepay.

AS-22 (❼)

Explain cash flow.

Application Questions

AP-1 (❸, ❼)

Jessica recently started her own shoe repair business. The following are the transactions during the first month of operations (June 2011):

1. Jessica invested money in the business.	$10,000
2. Paid two months of rent in advance.	1,000
3. Purchased store appliances for cash.	3,000
4. Incurred business registration expenses, paid with cash.	600
5. Paid travel expenses with cash.	1,100
6. Made cash sales during the month.	2,300
7. Paid salary to an assistant.	600
8. Borrowed money from the bank.	3,000
9. Received bills for electricity, water and telephone, to be paid next month.	800
10. Jessica withdrew cash for personal purposes.	500

Required: Post the above transactions to the T-Account worksheet.

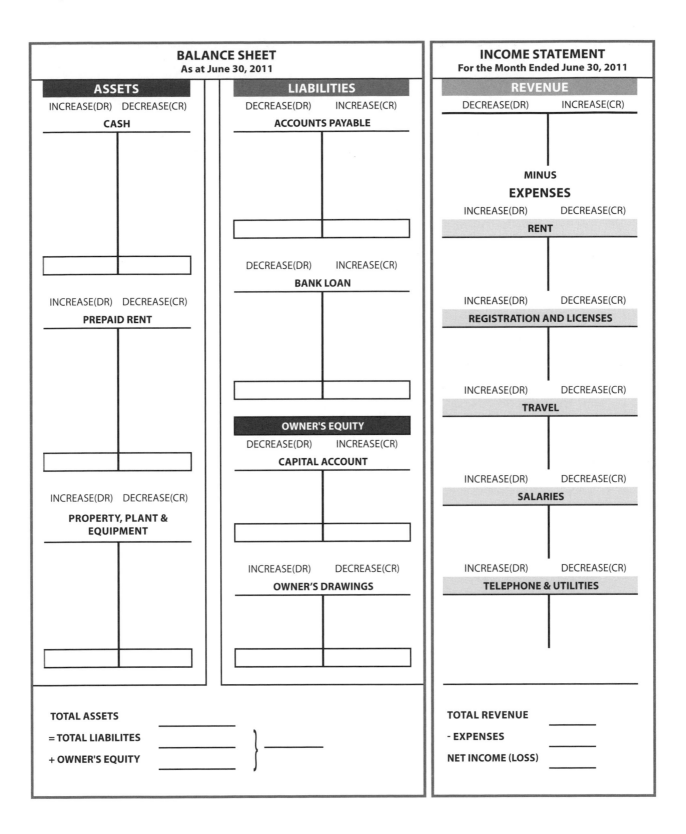

BALANCE SHEET
As at June 30, 2011

ASSETS

INCREASE(DR) DECREASE(CR)
CASH

INCREASE(DR) DECREASE(CR)
PREPAID RENT

INCREASE(DR) DECREASE(CR)
PROPERTY, PLANT & EQUIPMENT

LIABILITIES

DECREASE(DR) INCREASE(CR)
ACCOUNTS PAYABLE

DECREASE(DR) INCREASE(CR)
BANK LOAN

OWNER'S EQUITY

DECREASE(DR) INCREASE(CR)
CAPITAL ACCOUNT

INCREASE(DR) DECREASE(CR)
OWNER'S DRAWINGS

TOTAL ASSETS ______

= TOTAL LIABILITES ______

+ OWNER'S EQUITY ______ } ______

INCOME STATEMENT
For the Month Ended June 30, 2011

REVENUE

DECREASE(DR) INCREASE(CR)

MINUS

EXPENSES

INCREASE(DR) DECREASE(CR)
RENT

INCREASE(DR) DECREASE(CR)
REGISTRATION AND LICENSES

INCREASE(DR) DECREASE(CR)
TRAVEL

INCREASE(DR) DECREASE(CR)
SALARIES

INCREASE(DR) DECREASE(CR)
TELEPHONE & UTILITIES

TOTAL REVENUE ______

- EXPENSES ______

NET INCOME (LOSS) ______

AP-2 (❸, ❼)

Edward decided to start his own rent-a-car business after graduation, instead of looking for a job. The following are the transactions during the first month of operations (January 2011):

1.	Edward invested money in the business.	$20,000
2.	Borrowed a loan from the bank.	20,000
3.	Purchased brand new car for business use with cash.	35,000
4.	Paid the principal of bank loan with cash.	2,000
5.	Paid for maintenance expense with cash.	800
6.	Paid monthly salaries for personnel with cash.	1,000
7.	Paid miscellaneous expenses with cash.	300
8.	Received service revenue in cash for the month.	8,000
9.	Received utilities bill for the month, payable next month.	600
10.	Paid monthly interest on the bank loan with cash.	200
11.	Paid insurance for the next five months in advance.	1,500
12.	Edward withdrew cash for personal use.	1,000

Required: Prepare the T-Account worksheet, income statement and balance sheet.

BALANCE SHEET
As at January 31, 2011

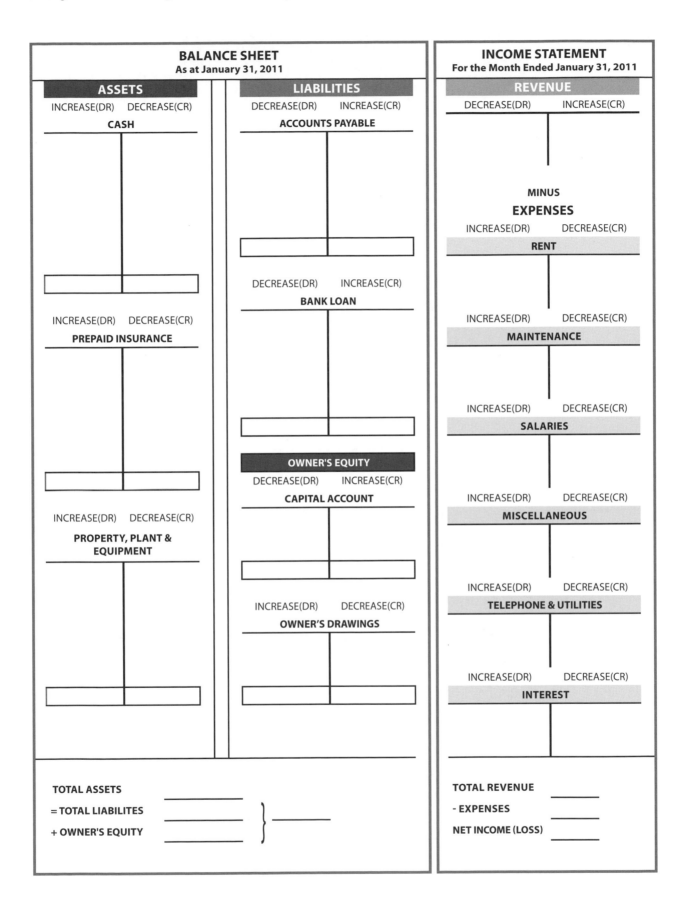

ASSETS

INCREASE(DR) DECREASE(CR)
CASH

INCREASE(DR) DECREASE(CR)
PREPAID INSURANCE

INCREASE(DR) DECREASE(CR)
PROPERTY, PLANT & EQUIPMENT

LIABILITIES

DECREASE(DR) INCREASE(CR)
ACCOUNTS PAYABLE

DECREASE(DR) INCREASE(CR)
BANK LOAN

OWNER'S EQUITY

DECREASE(DR) INCREASE(CR)
CAPITAL ACCOUNT

INCREASE(DR) DECREASE(CR)
OWNER'S DRAWINGS

TOTAL ASSETS ______

= TOTAL LIABILITES ______

+ OWNER'S EQUITY ______ } ______

INCOME STATEMENT
For the Month Ended January 31, 2011

REVENUE

DECREASE(DR) INCREASE(CR)

MINUS

EXPENSES

INCREASE(DR) DECREASE(CR)
RENT

INCREASE(DR) DECREASE(CR)
MAINTENANCE

INCREASE(DR) DECREASE(CR)
SALARIES

INCREASE(DR) DECREASE(CR)
MISCELLANEOUS

INCREASE(DR) DECREASE(CR)
TELEPHONE & UTILITIES

INCREASE(DR) DECREASE(CR)
INTEREST

TOTAL REVENUE ______

- EXPENSES ______

NET INCOME (LOSS) ______

Edward's Rent-A-Car Income Statement For the Month Ended January 31, 2011	

Edward's Rent-A-Car Balance Sheet As at January 31, 2011			

AP-3 (❸, ❼)

Health-Plus Clinic is a medical clinic that started operations in January 2010. Consider the following opening balances as of January 1, 2011.

Cash	$15,000
Prepaid Rent	6,000
Prepaid Insurance (separate from prepaid rent)	5,000
Property, Plant & Equipment	30,000
Accounts Payable	3,000
Bank Loan	10,000
Owner's Equity	43,000

The following are the transactions during the whole month of January:

1.	Purchased plane tickets for travelling with cash.	$1,500
2.	Paid cash to reduce the balance of accounts payable.	3,000
3.	The owner invested additional capital in the company.	5,000
4.	Purchased equipment with a bank loan.	4,000
5.	Paid cash for maintenance expenses.	1,000
6.	Earned revenue from patients on a cash basis.	15,000
7.	Received a bill for utilities used during the month. A cheque was issued to pay the bill immediately.	900
8.	Recognized prepaid rent as an expense.	2,000
9.	Paid interest for the month of January with cash.	100
10.	Paid monthly salaries to all medical practitioners and clinic personnel.	4,000
11.	The owner withdrew cash from the business to pay for personal expenses.	2,000

Required: Prepare the T-Account worksheet, income statement and balance sheet.

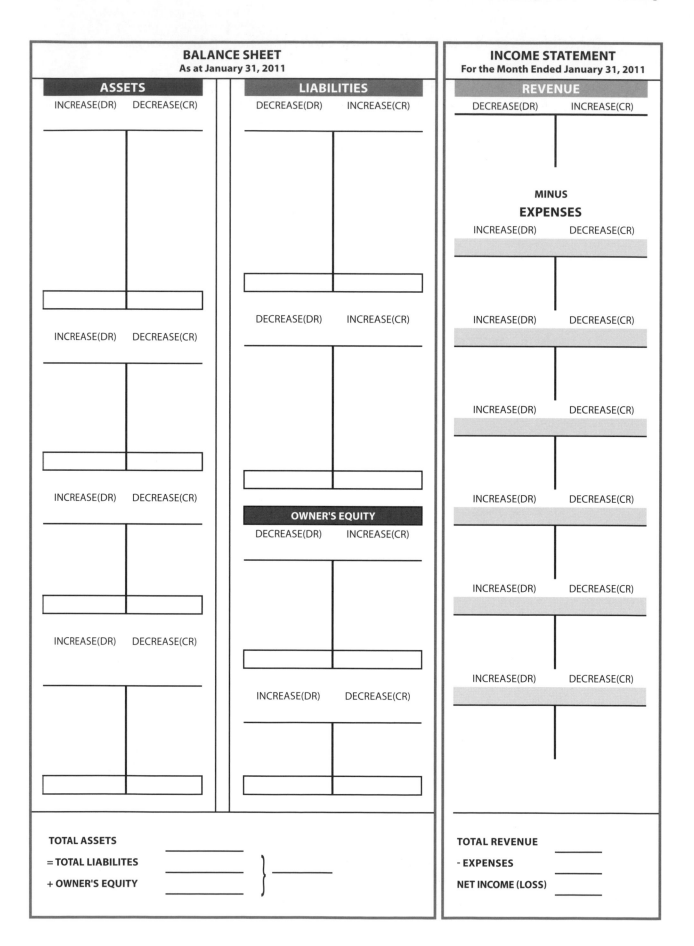

BALANCE SHEET
As at January 31, 2011

ASSETS

INCREASE(DR)	DECREASE(CR)

INCREASE(DR)	DECREASE(CR)

INCREASE(DR)	DECREASE(CR)

INCREASE(DR)	DECREASE(CR)

LIABILITIES

DECREASE(DR)	INCREASE(CR)

DECREASE(DR)	INCREASE(CR)

OWNER'S EQUITY

DECREASE(DR)	INCREASE(CR)

INCREASE(DR)	DECREASE(CR)

TOTAL ASSETS ________

= TOTAL LIABILITES ________ } ________

+ OWNER'S EQUITY ________

INCOME STATEMENT
For the Month Ended January 31, 2011

REVENUE

DECREASE(DR)	INCREASE(CR)

MINUS

EXPENSES

INCREASE(DR)	DECREASE(CR)

INCREASE(DR)	DECREASE(CR)

INCREASE(DR)	DECREASE(CR)

INCREASE(DR)	DECREASE(CR)

INCREASE(DR)	DECREASE(CR)

INCREASE(DR)	DECREASE(CR)

TOTAL REVENUE ________

- EXPENSES ________

NET INCOME (LOSS) ________

Health-Plus Clinic Income Statement For the Month Ended January 31, 2011	

Health-Plus Clinic Balance Sheet As at January 31, 2011			

AP-4 (❸, ❼)

For each transaction, indicate whether the total assets (A), liabilities (L) or owner's equity (OE) increased (+), decreased (-) or did not change (o) by placing the sign in the appropriate column.

	A	L	OE
1. Paid salaries for current month.			
2. Purchased equipment on credit.			
3. Purchased furniture using cash.			
4. Additional investment into the business.			
5. Received payment for services provided.			
6. Made partial payment for equipment purchased on credit.			
7. Billed customers for services performed.			
8. Withdrew cash for personal use.			
9. Received payment from customers already billed.			
10. Received bills for utilities to be paid next month.			

AP-5 (❸, ❼)

Sheila opened a dormitory locator business called Dormitory Locators near a college campus. During the first month of operations, June 2011, Sheila had the following transactions:

1. Invested $10,000 of personal funds to start the business.
2. Incurred travel expenses for $650, which will be paid next month.
3. Paid $700 cash for maintenance expense.
4. Received $5,000 cash for services provided to clients.
5. Made the $650 payment for travel expenses purchased on account in transaction 2.
6. Paid three months of office rent costing $1,500 in advance.
7. Incurred $300 of utilities expense, which will be paid next month.
8. Recognized one month of office rent that was previously prepaid.
9. Sheila withdrew $1,000 cash for personal use.
10. Purchased second-hand car worth $10,000 for business use with cash.

Required: Prepare a T-Account worksheet.

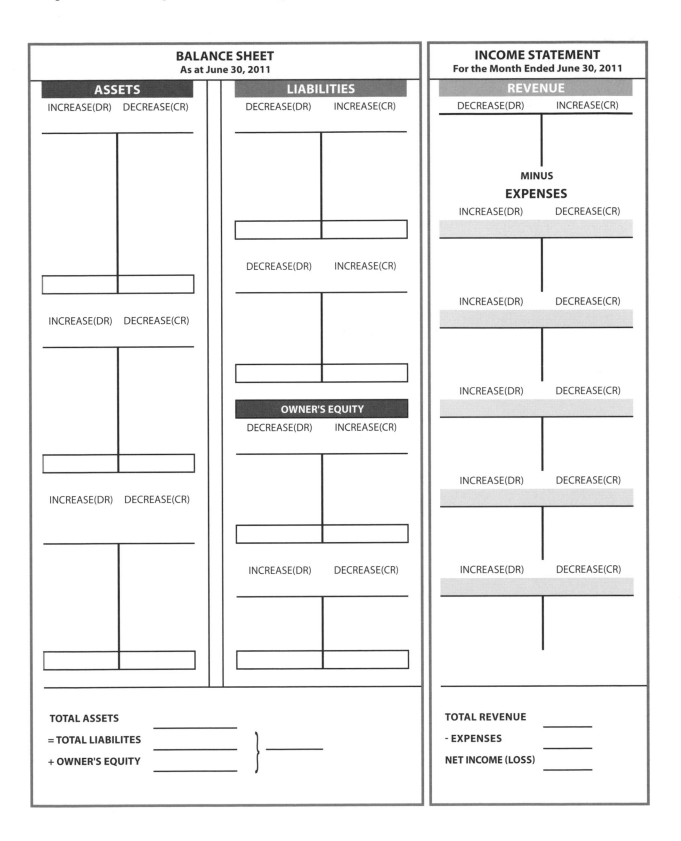

BALANCE SHEET
As at June 30, 2011

ASSETS

INCREASE(DR) DECREASE(CR)

INCREASE(DR) DECREASE(CR)

INCREASE(DR) DECREASE(CR)

LIABILITIES

DECREASE(DR) INCREASE(CR)

DECREASE(DR) INCREASE(CR)

OWNER'S EQUITY

DECREASE(DR) INCREASE(CR)

INCREASE(DR) DECREASE(CR)

TOTAL ASSETS ______

= TOTAL LIABILITES ______

+ OWNER'S EQUITY ______ } ______

INCOME STATEMENT
For the Month Ended June 30, 2011

REVENUE

DECREASE(DR) INCREASE(CR)

MINUS

EXPENSES

INCREASE(DR) DECREASE(CR)

INCREASE(DR) DECREASE(CR)

INCREASE(DR) DECREASE(CR)

INCREASE(DR) DECREASE(CR)

INCREASE(DR) DECREASE(CR)

TOTAL REVENUE ______

- EXPENSES ______

NET INCOME (LOSS) ______

AP-6 (❸)

For each of the given transactions, determine the effect on owner's equity by placing a checkmark in the space provided.

	Effect on Owner's Equity		
	Increase	Decrease	No Effect
1. Invested money in the business.			
2. Purchased equipment on account.			
3. Paid one-third of the amount owing for the purchase of equipment.			
4. Received cash for the services rendered.			
5. Paid salaries for the month.			
6. Withdrew cash for personal use.			
7. Paid monthly rent.			
8. Additional investment by the owner.			
9. Purchased supplies using cash.			
10. Acquired land using cash.			

AP-7 (❸, ❼)

The given transactions were completed by Juliet's Delivery Services during May 2011. Indicate the effects of each transaction by placing the appropriate letter in the space provided.

a. Increase in asset, decrease in another asset
b. Increase in asset, increase in liability
c. Increase in asset, increase in owner's equity
d. Decrease in asset, decrease in liability
e. Decrease in asset, decrease in owner's equity

_____ 1. Received cash for providing delivery services.
_____ 2. Paid amount owing that was outstanding to a creditor.
_____ 3. Invested additional cash in the business.
_____ 4. Paid advertising expense with cash.
_____ 5. Billed customers for delivery services on account.
_____ 6. Purchased office furniture on account.
_____ 7. Paid rent for the month.
_____ 8. Received cash from customers on account.
_____ 9. Obtained bank loan.
_____ 10. Owner withdrew cash for personal use.

AP-8 (❸, ❼)

For the following transactions, fill in the table on the right with the two accounts related to each transaction.

TRANSACTIONS	ACCOUNT TITLE 1.	2.
1. Invested cash in the business.		
2. Purchased service vehicle for business use.		
3. Collected cash for services provided this week.		
4. Provided services this week on credit.		
5. Paid operating expenses in cash.		
6. Received a bill for operating services incurred this week.		
7. Borrowed a car loan.		
8. Collected cash on accounts receivable for services provided previously.		
9. Paid monthly salaries to employees with cash.		
10. Incurred operating expenses this week, to be paid next month.		
11. Paid cash on accounts payable for expenses incurred previously.		
12. Paid cash for an insurance policy expiring after two years.		

AP-9 (❸, ❼)

Jeff Roberts Communications is a public relations firm. On April 30, 2011, the firm had the following financial data:

Account balances	
Cash	$20,000
Prepaid Rent	10,000
Property, Plant & Equipment	25,000
Accounts Payable	8,000
Owner's Equity (Capital Account)	47,000

During the month of May, the company completed the following transactions:

1.	Purchased office equipment on account.	$800
2.	Paid amount owing that was outstanding to a supplier.	6,000
3.	Received cash from customers for services rendered.	5,000
4.	Paid utilities bill for May with cash.	700
5.	Purchased a computer on account.	1,500
6.	Received a bill to be paid in July for advertisements placed in a national newspaper during the month of May to promote Jeff Roberts Communications.	1,000
7.	Paid May's salaries with cash.	1,900
8.	Withdrew cash for personal use.	3,000
9.	Recognized rent for May (which was previously prepaid).	2,000

Required: Prepare the T-Account worksheet.

Note: the ending balance for the month of April is the opening balance for the month of May.

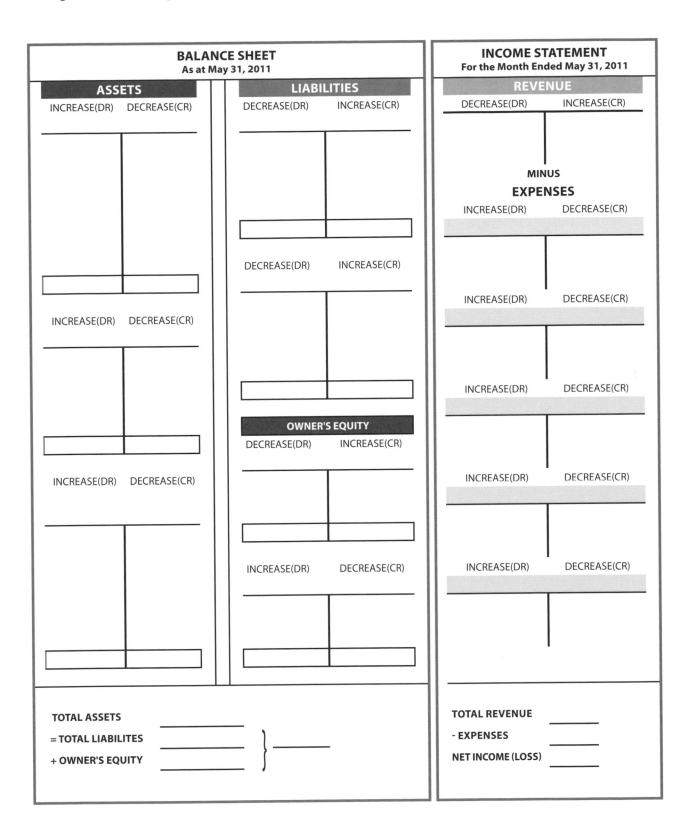

BALANCE SHEET
As at May 31, 2011

ASSETS

INCREASE(DR) DECREASE(CR)

INCREASE(DR) DECREASE(CR)

INCREASE(DR) DECREASE(CR)

LIABILITIES

DECREASE(DR) INCREASE(CR)

DECREASE(DR) INCREASE(CR)

OWNER'S EQUITY

DECREASE(DR) INCREASE(CR)

INCREASE(DR) DECREASE(CR)

TOTAL ASSETS ______

= TOTAL LIABILITES ______

+ OWNER'S EQUITY ______

INCOME STATEMENT
For the Month Ended May 31, 2011

REVENUE

DECREASE(DR) INCREASE(CR)

MINUS

EXPENSES

INCREASE(DR) DECREASE(CR)

INCREASE(DR) DECREASE(CR)

INCREASE(DR) DECREASE(CR)

INCREASE(DR) DECREASE(CR)

INCREASE(DR) DECREASE(CR)

TOTAL REVENUE ______

- EXPENSES ______

NET INCOME (LOSS) ______

AP-10 (❸, ❼)

On December 1, 2010, Mary Ann established City Laundry. During the first month, the following transactions occurred:

TRANSACTIONS

1. Mary Ann deposited $15,000 into City Laundry's bank account.
2. Bought tables and chairs worth $1,000 with cash.
3. Received and paid utilities bill for $1,200 in cash.
4. Purchased washers and dryers for a total of $4,000; where $2,000 is the down payment and the remainder is due in 30 days.
5. Purchased two additional dryers worth $1,100 from Marky Distributors, on account.
6. Made cash sales of $4,000 in the first half of the month.
7. Paid $900 cash for a one-year insurance policy.
8. Paid $1,000 cash for current month's rent.
9. Paid the amount owing to Marky Distributors.
10. Made cash sales of $3,500 in the second half of the month.
11. Paid employee salaries of $1,400.
12. Withdrew $2,000 cash for personal use.
13. Recorded first month's insurance expense of $75.

Required: Prepare the T-Account worksheet.

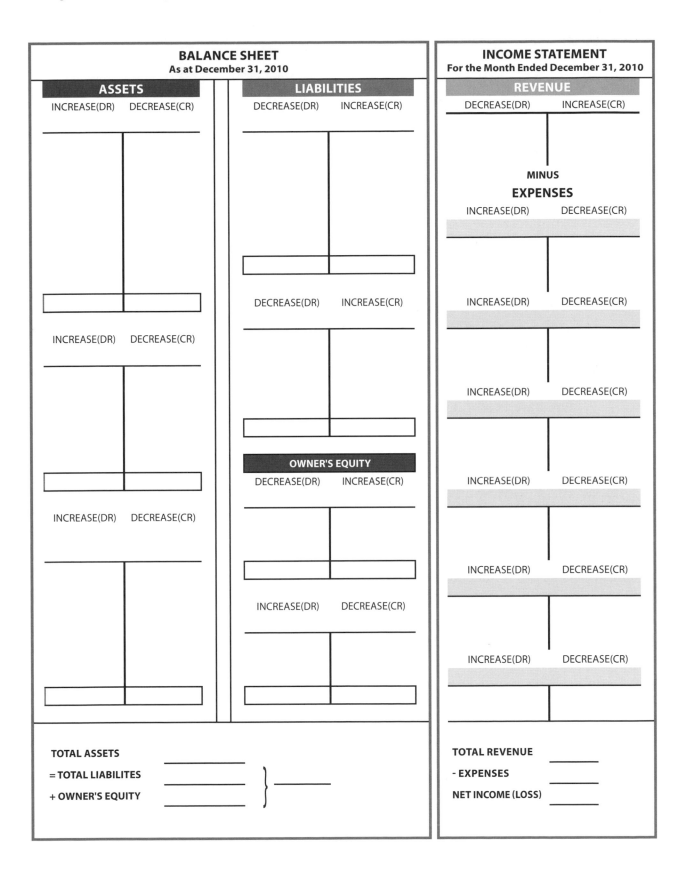

BALANCE SHEET
As at December 31, 2010

ASSETS

INCREASE(DR) DECREASE(CR)

INCREASE(DR) DECREASE(CR)

INCREASE(DR) DECREASE(CR)

LIABILITIES

DECREASE(DR) INCREASE(CR)

DECREASE(DR) INCREASE(CR)

OWNER'S EQUITY

DECREASE(DR) INCREASE(CR)

INCREASE(DR) DECREASE(CR)

TOTAL ASSETS ______

= TOTAL LIABILITES ______

+ OWNER'S EQUITY ______

INCOME STATEMENT
For the Month Ended December 31, 2010

REVENUE

DECREASE(DR) INCREASE(CR)

MINUS

EXPENSES

INCREASE(DR) DECREASE(CR)

INCREASE(DR) DECREASE(CR)

INCREASE(DR) DECREASE(CR)

INCREASE(DR) DECREASE(CR)

INCREASE(DR) DECREASE(CR)

INCREASE(DR) DECREASE(CR)

TOTAL REVENUE ______

- EXPENSES ______

NET INCOME (LOSS) ______

AP-11 (❸, ❼)

The balance sheet of Jessica's Computer Services on February 28, 2011 is shown below.

Jessica's Computer Services Balance Sheet As at February 28, 2011			
Assets		**Liabilities**	
Cash	$4,000	Accounts Payable	$3,000
Prepaid Insurance	3,000	Bank Loan	0
Property, Plant & Equipment	25,000		
		Total Liabilities	**$3,000**
		Owner's Equity	**$29,000**
Total Assets	**$32,000**	**Total Libilities and Owner's Equity**	**$32,000**

During March, the business engaged in the following transactions:

1. Borrowed a $20,000 bank loan.
2. Purchased computer equipment for $5,000 cash.
3. Performed services for a customer and received $4,000 cash.
4. Purchased furniture for $1,000 on credit.
5. Paid $1,500 to a supplier for the amount owed.
6. Paid the following expenses in cash: salaries, $1,000; rent, $1,500; and interest, $200.
7. Received a $900 utilities bill, due next month.
8. Withdrew $3,500 cash for personal use.

Required: Prepare the T-Account worksheet, income statement and balance sheet.

Note: the ending balance for the month of February is the opening balance for the month of March.

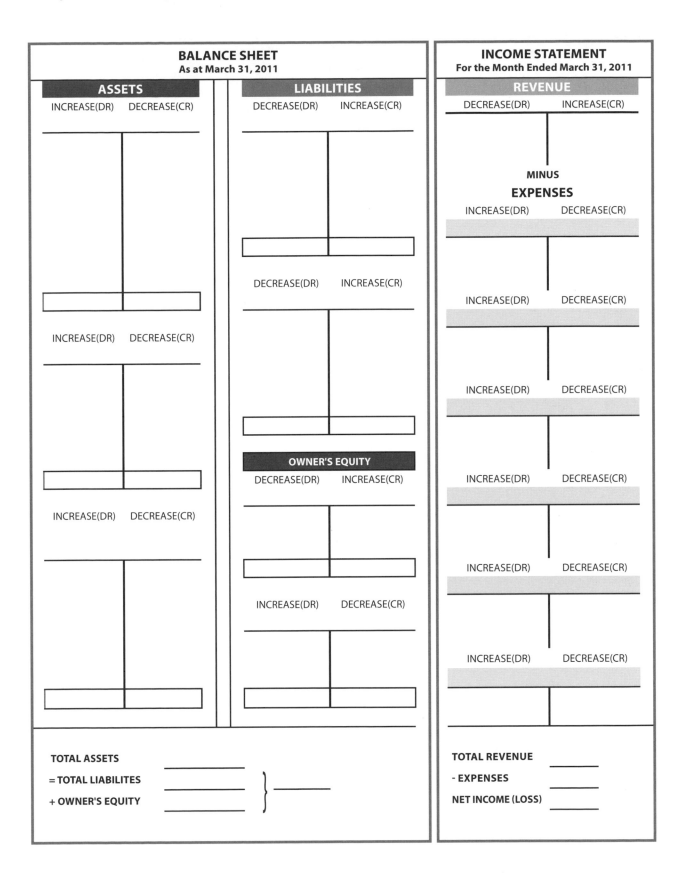

BALANCE SHEET
As at March 31, 2011

ASSETS

INCREASE(DR) DECREASE(CR)

INCREASE(DR) DECREASE(CR)

INCREASE(DR) DECREASE(CR)

LIABILITIES

DECREASE(DR) INCREASE(CR)

DECREASE(DR) INCREASE(CR)

OWNER'S EQUITY

DECREASE(DR) INCREASE(CR)

INCREASE(DR) DECREASE(CR)

TOTAL ASSETS ______

= TOTAL LIABILITES ______

+ OWNER'S EQUITY ______

INCOME STATEMENT
For the Month Ended March 31, 2011

REVENUE

DECREASE(DR) INCREASE(CR)

MINUS

EXPENSES

INCREASE(DR) DECREASE(CR)

INCREASE(DR) DECREASE(CR)

INCREASE(DR) DECREASE(CR)

INCREASE(DR) DECREASE(CR)

INCREASE(DR) DECREASE(CR)

INCREASE(DR) DECREASE(CR)

TOTAL REVENUE ______

- EXPENSES ______

NET INCOME (LOSS) ______

Jessica's Computer Services Income Statement For the Month Ended March 31, 20011	

Jessica's Computer Services Balance Sheet As at March 31, 2011			

AP-12 (❷, ❸)

The following is a list of Double Duplicator's accounts and balances as at March 31, 2010.

Cash	$2,700
Owner's Equity (Capital Account)	2,000
Accounts Payable	5,000
Prepaid Insurance	2,300
Bank Loan	10,000
Automobile Loan	18,000
Prepaid Rent	5,000
Property, Plant & Equipment	25,000

Required: Prepare a balance sheet using the above information.

Double Duplicators Balance Sheet As at March 31, 2010			

AP-13 (❸, ❼)

Christine Jacob is a financial planning consultant. During the month of February, she completed the following transactions:

1. Christine invested $8,000 cash in the business.
2. Paid $1,400 cash for February office rent.
3. Received $6,500 from a client for services rendered.
4. Paid $500 cash to Shell Super Service for gas purchases.
5. Paid $700 cash to Helpful Manpower Services for consulting services.
6. Purchased office equipment worth $900 on account.
7. Owner withdrew $2,500 cash for personal use.
8. Donated $800 cash to the National Red Cross.
9. Received $2,000 cash from another client for services rendered.
10. Made partial payment of $500 on the equipment that were purchased on account.

Required: Prepare the T-Account worksheet.

BALANCE SHEET
As at February 28, 2011

ASSETS

INCREASE(DR) DECREASE(CR)

INCREASE(DR) DECREASE(CR)

INCREASE(DR) DECREASE(CR)

LIABILITIES

DECREASE(DR) INCREASE(CR)

DECREASE(DR) INCREASE(CR)

OWNER'S EQUITY

DECREASE(DR) INCREASE(CR)

INCREASE(DR) DECREASE(CR)

TOTAL ASSETS ________

= TOTAL LIABILITES ________

+ OWNER'S EQUITY ________ } ________

INCOME STATEMENT
For the Month Ended February, 2011

REVENUE

DECREASE(DR) INCREASE(CR)

MINUS

EXPENSES

INCREASE(DR) DECREASE(CR)

INCREASE(DR) DECREASE(CR)

INCREASE(DR) DECREASE(CR)

INCREASE(DR) DECREASE(CR)

INCREASE(DR) DECREASE(CR)

TOTAL REVENUE ________

- EXPENSES ________

NET INCOME (LOSS) ________

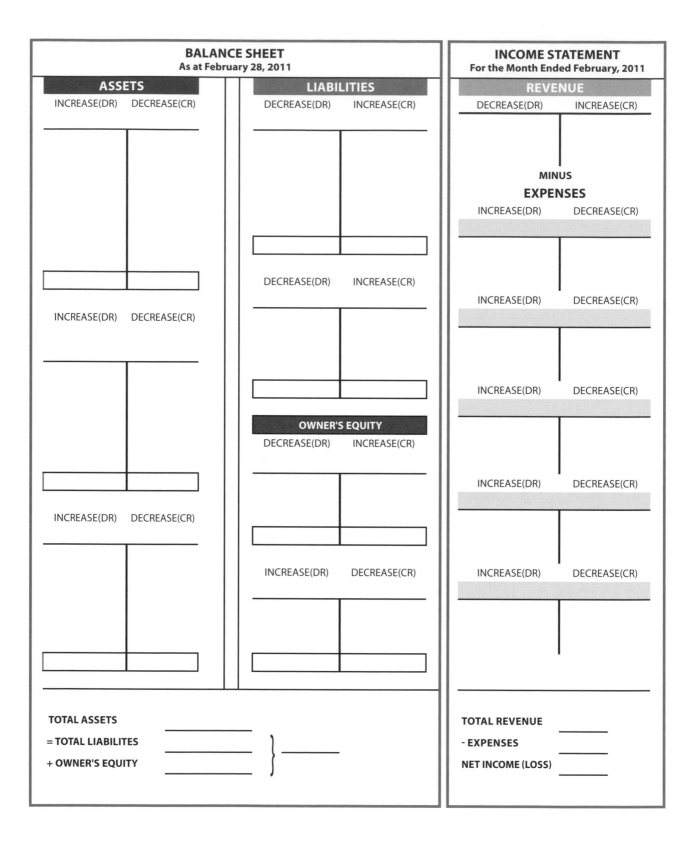

AP-14 (❸, ❼)

On April 1, 2011, Aaron established a business to manage rental properties. He had the following transactions during its first month of operations:

1. Made a deposit into the business bank account. $20,000
2. Purchased office equipment on account. 1,000
3. Received cash for managing rental properties for a client. 5,000
4. Purchased a TV on account. 350
5. Paid utilities bill for the month in cash. 400
6. Borrowed a bank loan and used that money to purchase office furniture. 5,000
7. Paid cash to reduce the amount of bank loan principal. 500
8. Paid rent for the month with cash. 1,800
9. Paid office staff salaries. 1,500
10. Withdrew cash for personal use. 1,000

Required: Prepare the T-Account worksheet.

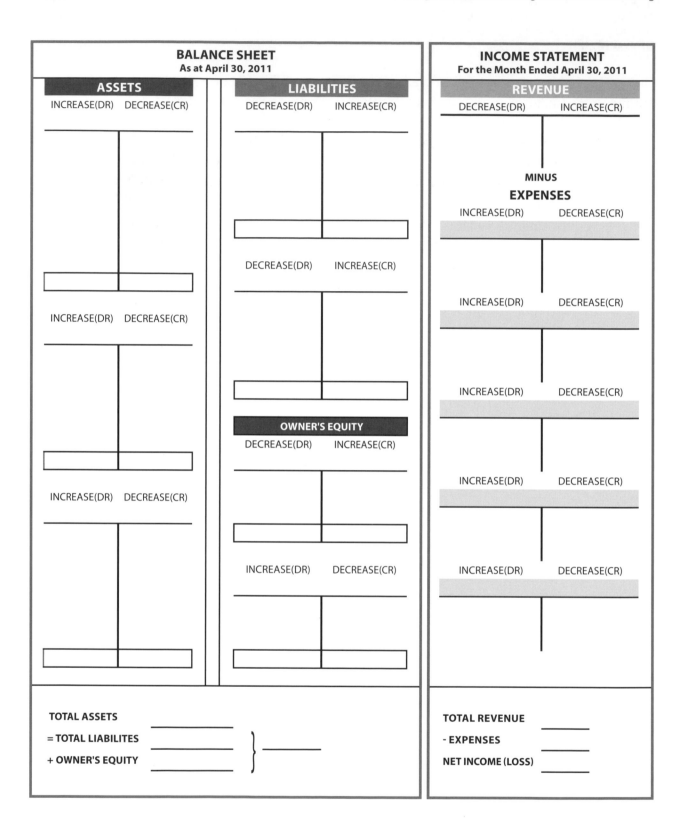

BALANCE SHEET
As at April 30, 2011

ASSETS

INCREASE(DR) DECREASE(CR)

INCREASE(DR) DECREASE(CR)

INCREASE(DR) DECREASE(CR)

LIABILITIES

DECREASE(DR) INCREASE(CR)

DECREASE(DR) INCREASE(CR)

OWNER'S EQUITY

DECREASE(DR) INCREASE(CR)

INCREASE(DR) DECREASE(CR)

TOTAL ASSETS

= TOTAL LIABILITES

+ OWNER'S EQUITY

INCOME STATEMENT
For the Month Ended April 30, 2011

REVENUE

DECREASE(DR) INCREASE(CR)

MINUS

EXPENSES

INCREASE(DR) DECREASE(CR)

INCREASE(DR) DECREASE(CR)

INCREASE(DR) DECREASE(CR)

INCREASE(DR) DECREASE(CR)

INCREASE(DR) DECREASE(CR)

TOTAL REVENUE

- EXPENSES

NET INCOME (LOSS)

AP-15 (❸, ❼)

Troy, an architect, opened his own business on March 1, 2011. During the month, he completed the following transactions related to his professional practice:

1.	Transferred cash from personal bank account to the business account.	$30,000
2.	Provided services for cash.	3,000
3.	Purchased office and computer equipment on account, which will be paid next month.	8,000
4.	Paid cash for meals and entertainment.	1,100
5.	Paid insurance expense with cash.	800
6.	Received cash from clients for delivering finished plans.	4,000
7.	Paid cash for miscellaneous expenses.	600
8.	Received utilities bill, to be paid next month.	1,000
9.	Paid cash for office rent for the month of March.	1,200
10.	Paid salary to assistant.	1,000

Required: Prepare the T-Account worksheet.

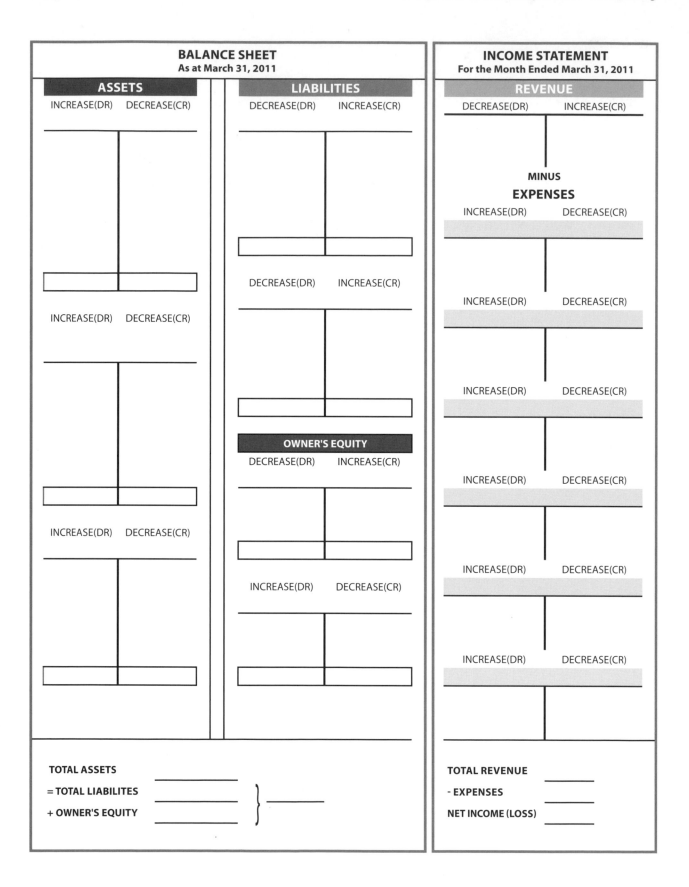

BALANCE SHEET
As at March 31, 2011

ASSETS

INCREASE(DR) DECREASE(CR)

INCREASE(DR) DECREASE(CR)

INCREASE(DR) DECREASE(CR)

LIABILITIES

DECREASE(DR) INCREASE(CR)

DECREASE(DR) INCREASE(CR)

OWNER'S EQUITY

DECREASE(DR) INCREASE(CR)

INCREASE(DR) DECREASE(CR)

TOTAL ASSETS ______

= TOTAL LIABILITES ______

+ OWNER'S EQUITY ______

INCOME STATEMENT
For the Month Ended March 31, 2011

REVENUE

DECREASE(DR) INCREASE(CR)

MINUS

EXPENSES

INCREASE(DR) DECREASE(CR)

INCREASE(DR) DECREASE(CR)

INCREASE(DR) DECREASE(CR)

INCREASE(DR) DECREASE(CR)

INCREASE(DR) DECREASE(CR)

INCREASE(DR) DECREASE(CR)

TOTAL REVENUE ______

- EXPENSES ______

NET INCOME (LOSS) ______

AP-16 (❷)

Organize the following asset and liability accounts in the order they are likely to appear in a balance sheet.

Assets	Liabilities
Accounts Receivable	Bank Loan
Cash	Accounts Payable
Property, Plant & Equipment	
Prepaid Expenses	

AP-17 (❹)

Match each form of an organization with the appropriate description.

A	Sole proprietorship
B	Partnership
C	Cooperative
D	Corporation
E	Not-for-Profit Organization

____	A business that operates for the benefits of its members (the people who use its products and services).
____	This type of organization usually does not have an identifiable owner.
____	There are two types of this type of business: one of that limits the liability of the owners and one that does not.
____	A business operated by a single owner.
____	This type of business often elects a board of directors.

AP-18 (❺, ❻)

Match each form of an organization with the appropriate description.

A	Merchandising
B	Service
C	Manufacturing

D	Internal Stakeholder
E	External Stakeholder

____ A law firm is an example of this type of business.

____ The owner of a business is an example of a(n) ____________.

____ This type of business buys goods to resell to customers.

____ An automaker is an example of this type of business.

____ A company's supplier is an example of a(n) ___________.

Case Study

CS-1 (❸, ❹, ❺, ❼)

Granyard Clockworks is a service company that repairs damaged watches and clocks. The company has a year end of December 31 and it is owned fully by John Granyard. John is fully liable for all activities of the business. In the most recent month (May 2011), Granyard Clockworks had the following transactions:

1. John deposited additional cash into the business in the amount of $40,000
2. Borrowed $15,000 in cash from the bank
3. Paid $3,500 cash for May's rent
4. Paid $6,000 in salaries for May
5. Performed services and earned $18,000 in cash
6. Incurred telephone expenses of $500 (to be paid next month)
7. Prepaid insurance for one year in the amount of $11,000
8. Incurred maintenance expense of $1,000 (paid on account)
9. John withdrew $5,000 from the business for personal use

As at April 30, 2011, the account balances for Granyard Clockworks' were as follows:

Cash: $50,000	Accounts Payable: $2,000
Accounts Receivable: $12,000	Bank Loan: $60,000
Prepaid Insurance: $800	Owner's Equity (Capital Account): $40,800
Property, Plant & Equipment: $40,000	

Required:

a) Complete the T-Account worksheets for May 2011 (provided below) for each of the balance sheet and income statement.

GRANYARD CLOCKWORKS
BALANCE SHEET
AS AT MAY 31, 2011

Assets

INCREASE (DR)	DECREASE (CR)
Opening:	
Ending	

INCREASE (DR)	DECREASE (CR)
Opening:	
Ending	

INCREASE (DR)	DECREASE (CR)
Opening:	
Ending	

INCREASE (DR)	DECREASE (CR)
Opening:	
Ending	

Liabilities

DECREASE (DR)	INCREASE (CR)
	Opening:
	Ending

DECREASE (DR)	INCREASE (CR)
	Opening:
	Ending

Owner's Equity

DECREASE (DR)	INCREASE (CR)
	Opening:
	Ending

INCREASE (DR)	DECREASE (CR)
Opening:	
Ending	

Total Assets	
= Total Liabilities	
+ Owner's Eqauity	

GRANYARD CLOCKWORKS
INCOME STATEMENT
FOR THE MONTH ENDED MAY 31, 2011

DECREASE (DR)	**REVENUE**	INCREASE (CR)

Minus
EXPENSES

INCREASE (DR)	DECREASE (CR)

INCREASE (DR)	DECREASE (CR)

INCREASE (DR)	DECREASE (CR)

INCREASE (DR)	DECREASE (CR)

INCREASE (DR)	DECREASE (CR)

INCREASE (DR)	DECREASE (CR)

Total Revenue	
Total Expenses	
Surplus (Deficit)	

b) What form of an organization is Granyard Clockworks? Explain.

c) Is John Granyard an internal or external stakeholder?

d) If John Granyard were to sell all of the assets of the business for cash on May 31, 2011 and use the cash to pay off the company's debts, what is the remaining amount? What does it represent?

Chapter 3

ACCOUNTING PRINCIPLES AND PRACTICES IN A BUSINESS

Assessment Questions

AS-1 (❶)

Briefly explain financial accounting.

____

____

____

AS-2 (❶)

Briefly explain managerial accounting.

____

____

____

AS-3 (❷)

Define GAAP. Which entity is responsible for the development and communication of Canadian GAAP?

____

____

____

____

AS-4 (❷)

According to GAAP, what are the four characteristics of effective and useful information?

____

____

AS-5 (❷)

Describe the characteristic of relevance.

____

____

____

____

AS-6 (❷)

Describe timeliness. Which characteristic is timeliness a component of?

____

____

____

AS-7 (❷)

Describe the characteristic of reliability.

____

____

____

____

AS-8 (❷)

What is verifiability? Which characteristic is verifiability a component of?

AS-9 (❷)

Describe the characteristic of understandability.

AS-10 (❷)

Describe the characteristic of comparability.

AS-11 (❷)

What is a trade-off?

AS-12 (❷)

Provide an example of a commonly known trade-off.

AS-13 (❸)

What does the business entity principle state?

AS-14 (❸)

What is the going concern principle?

AS-15 (❸)

Describe the monetary unit principle.

AS-16 (❸)

Describe the objectivity principle.

AS-17 (❸)

What is the cost principle?

AS-18 (❸)

What does the conservatism principle state?

AS-19 (❸)

Explain the time period principle.

AS-20 (❸)

Explain the revenue recognition principle.

AS-21 (❸)

Describe the matching principle.

AS-22 (❸)

What is the consistency principle?

____

____

____

AS-23 (❸)

What does that materiality principle state?

____

____

____

AS-24 (❸)

Explain the full disclosure principle.

____

____

____

AS-25 (❹)

What is IFRS? What is its purpose?

____

____

____

____

AS-26 (❹)

Explain the two general similarities between GAAP and IFRS.

AS-27 (❺)

Identify two advantages of IFRS.

AS-28 (❺)

Identify two disadvantages of IFRS.

AS-29 (❻)

Define controls.

AS-30 (❻)

What is the purpose of internal controls?

AS-31 (❼)

List two ethical standards for accountants.

Application Questions

AP-1 (❷)

Match each of the following characteristics of information to the appropriate description in the table below.

- Relevance
- Reliability
- Understandability
- Comparability
- Timeliness
- Verifiability

Term (fill in)	**Description**
	Information is free from material error and bias
	A component of relevance
	The financial statements of a company should be prepared in a similar way year after year
	A component of reliability
	Financial information can be reasonably understood by its users
	All information for decision making is present in the financial statements

AP-2 (❷)

Hawkton Publishing Corporation is a publisher of math textbooks. The company is a large, well-known publicly traded corporation with thousands of shareholders. It produces financial statements on an annual basis. The most recent financial statements (for the year ended December 31, 2010) showed comparative balances for 2010 and 2009. The 2010 balances were derived using accrual-based accounting whereas the 2009 balances were derived using cash-based accounting. Which characteristic(s) of information did Hawkton fail to represent? Explain.

AP-3 (❷)

Reflex Sports Inc. is a manufacturer of sports equipment for children. They rely on GAAP to prepare their financial statements. The nature of their accounting transactions can be quite complex at times. However, the financial statements have no additional notes to support them. The company also does not keep all invoices on record to back up expense amounts reported on the financial statements. Which characteristic(s) of information did Reflex Sports fail to represent? Explain.

____

____

____

____

____

AP-4 (❸)

Match each of the following basic GAAP and IFRS concepts and principles to the appropriate description in the table below.

- Business entity principle
- Going concern principle
- Monetary unit principle
- Objectivity principle
- Cost principle
- Conservatism principle

Term (fill in)	**Description**
	The accountant should exercise the option that results in a lower balance of assets, lower net income or a higher balance of debt.
	Accounting transactions should be recorded on the basis of verifiable evidence.
	Assumes that a business will continue to operate into the foreseeable future.
	Financial reports should be expressed in a single currency.
	Accounting for a business must be kept separate from the personal affairs of its owner or any other business.
	Accounting for purchases must be recorded at their values on the date of purchase.

AP-5 (❸)

Match each of the following basic GAAP and IFRS concepts and principles to the appropriate description in the table below.

- Time period principle
- Revenue recognition principle
- Matching principle
- Consistency principle
- Materiality principle
- Full disclosure principle

Term (fill in)	**Description**
	Accounting takes place over specific fiscal periods.
	Prevents people from changing accounting methods for the sole purpose of manipulating figures on the financial statements.
	Sales must be recorded (recognized) at the time the duties are performed.
	Any and all information that affects the full understanding of a company's financial statements must be included with the financial statements.
	An expense must be recorded in the same accounting period in which it was used to produce revenue.
	Accountants should use GAAP except when doing so would be more expensive or complicated relative to the value of the transaction.

AP-6 (❸)

Alton Floral Inc. is a recently incorporated company that operates in the gardening industry. The owner of the company has decided not to hire an accountant but instead maintain the accounting records on his own. He has included his employees as assets on the balance sheet in the account "Human Resources". He has valued them at the present value of their future salaries on the balance sheet. Also, the financial statements are not supported by notes explaining some of the figures. Which of the basic concepts and principles of GAAP has Alton Floral violated? Explain.

____

____

____

____

____

AP-7 (❸)

Mackenzie Attire Corporation is currently preparing their annual financial statements for the past fiscal year. The company uses cash-based accounting. The company's policy includes receiving payment for its services well before the service is performed. The owner recently purchased a fish tank for his home and the transaction included a decrease to Mackenzie Attire's equity (an expense was recorded in the income statement). The value of inventory is adjusted annually to be stated at fair value. Which of the basic concepts and principles of GAAP has Mackenzie Attire violated? Explain.

____

____

____

____

____

____

____

____

____

____

AP-8 (❷, ❸)

For each basic concept/principle of GAAP, indicate which one of the four characteristics of information it is most related to.

Characteristic (fill in)	**Basic Concept or Principle**
	Monetary Unit Principle
	Objectivity Principle
	Cost Principle
	Consistency Principle
	Materiality Principle
	Full Disclosure Principle

AP-9 (❸)

Suppose that company has changed its policy for depreciation from one year to the next. An employee in the accounting department addressed this change with the owner. The employee asked the owner why the accounting policy was changed and why the reasoning for the change was not disclosed in the financial statements. The owner replied, "IFRS gives you the option to use a different depreciation method from one year to the next. We also are not required to explain our choices." Is the owner correct in his reasoning? Explain.

____

____

____

____

____

____

AP-10 (❸)

The accountant for GYC Consultants is facing an important accounting decision. The company recently incurred a material transaction that can be accounted for in three different ways (options A, B, and C). The effect on the company's net income and total assets for each option is shown below. In the spirit of GAAP, which option should GYC's accountant choose to account for the transaction and why?

Effect on:	Option A	Option B	Option C
Net Income	+$5,200	+$4,100	+$4,600
Total Assets	+$1,100	+$900	+$1,000

____

____

____

____

____

AP-11 (❹)

Heath Trek Company has four different asset accounts: property, plant & equipment, accounts receivable, short-term investments and cash. Shown below is the average amount of time required to turn each asset into cash.

Asset	Cash Turnover Time (in days)
Property, plant & equipment	5,480
Accounts receivable	60
Short-term investments	120
Cash	N/A

Required:

a) If Heath Trek's financial statements were prepared using GAAP, in which order will the assets be presented on the balance sheet?

____

____

____

____

b) If Heath Trek's financial statements were prepared using IFRS instead, in which order will the assets be presented on the balance sheet?

____

____

____

____

AP-12 (❹)

Starks Instruments Inc. has five different asset accounts: property, plant & equipment, inventory, cash, accounts receivable and prepaid expenses. Shown below is the level of liquidity of each asset.

Assset	Liquidity Level
Property, plant & equipment	Very low
Inventory	Medium
Cash	Very high
Accounts receivable	High
Prepaid expenses	Low

Required:

a) If Heath Trek's financial statements were prepared using GAAP, in which order will the assets be presented on the balance sheet?

____

____

____

b) If Heath Trek's financial statements were prepared using IFRS instead, in which order will the assets be presented on the balance sheet?

____

____

____

AP-13 (❻)

Effective internal controls are designed to address which of the following objectives?

(Check off):	Objective
	Safeguard assets
	Encourage good management
	Provide an accurate valuation of the company
	Cover up accounting errors
	Prevent and detect fraud error

AP-14 (⑥)

For each error or mishap below, identify a possible internal control that may have helped prevent it.

a) A cheque was issued to a supplier by a manufacturer as part of a major transaction. When the supplier tried to cash the cheque, there were insufficient funds in the manufacturer's bank account. Provide an internal control solution from the manufacturer's perspective.

____

____

____

____

b) A small business incurs only a few transactions every month. Its accounting clerk incorrectly entered the same transaction twice in the company's computerized accounting system. The error flowed through to the monthly financial statements.

____

____

____

____

c) A company incurs a few, significant cash transactions each day. The cash is deposited into the business's bank account on a bi-weekly basis. It was suspected that a disgruntled former employee stole a large sum of cash from the company's premises on the day he was fired.

____

____

____

____

AP-15 (❼)

Marcus is the senior accountant for a small accounting firm. He is currently performing the year end audit of a particular client: Le Jardin Oak Inc. (LJO), a manufacturer of high quality furniture. After Marcus had met with Le Jardin's CEO in a restaurant, the CEO noticed that Le Jardin's financial records, which were provided to Marcus, were scattered on the ground. At this point, the CEO was extremely disappointed since the records were meant for internal use only. Which ethical standard did Marcus violate? Explain.

____

____

____

____

____

Case Study

CS-1 (❷, ❸)

Gordon is the majority owner of Gordon House Restaurant (GHR), a publicly traded chain of family restaurants. The company is owned by hundreds of shareholders who expect timely, reliable and accurate financial statements. GHR produces financial statements periodically. It is now June 15, 2011. The accountant has prepared the financial statements for the eight-month period ended May 31, 2011. The previous financial statements covered a one year period.

The company was recently sued by another company, the details of which are not disclosed in the financial statements. The court proceedings have not yet ended. However, as of May 31, 2011, it was believed that GHR is very likely to lose the case and eventually pay a significant amount in damages to the plaintiff.

Also consider the following additional information:

- Cash disbursements are not supported by additional source documents
- GHR has recognized revenue at a different time than the costs associated with producing that revenue
- GHR has included the following statement in the supplementary information section of the financial statements: "In preparing the financial statements, Gordon House Restaurant has adhered to the conservatism principle. When judgement needs to be exercised, the option that results in the higher balance of assets, higher net income or lower balance of debt has been chosen."

Required:

a) Which of the four required characteristics of information has GHR failed to apply? Explain.

b) Which of the basic concepts and principles of accounting has GHR violated? Explain.

Chapter 4

REVENUE AND EXPENSE RECOGNITION

Assessment Questions

AS-1 (❶)

Define revenue.

AS-2 (❶)

What does it mean to *recognize* revenue?

AS-3 (❶)

What are the three possible ways revenue can be recognized?

AS-4 (❶)

What is the entry to record revenue if a customer pays *when* the service is delivered?

AS-5 (❶)

What is the entry to record revenue if a customer pays *after* the service is delivered?

AS-6 (❶)

What is the entry if a customer pays *before* the service is delivered? What is the entry to record revenue when the service is finally delivered?

AS-7 (❶)

What type of account is unearned revenue?

AS-8 (❷)

What are the three possible ways to pay for an expense?

AS-9 (❷)

What does it mean to *incur* an expense?

AS-10 (❷)

What is the entry to record an expense if a company pays *when* the expense is incurred?

____

____

AS-11 (❷)

What is the entry to record an expense if a company pays *after* the expense is incurred?

____

____

AS-12 (❷)

What is the entry if a company pays *before* the expense is incurred? What is the entry to record an expense when the expense is finally incurred?

____

____

____

____

AS-13 (❷)

How does a company decide whether to include office supplies as a prepaid expense on the balance sheet (an asset) or an expense on the income statement?

____

____

____

____

AS-14 (❸)

What is an accounting period?

____

____

AS-15 (❸)

State the purpose of adjustments.

AS-16 (❸)

What does accrual accounting state regarding revenue and expenses?

AS-17 (❹)

Provide four examples of adjustments.

AS-18 (❹)

Define accrued expenses.

AS-19 (❹)

What is the entry to recognize accrued interest expense?

AS-20 (❹)

Provide the entry to recognize depreciation expense at the end of accounting period.

AS-21 (❺)

If the original cost of a long-term asset is $9,000 and accumulated depreciation is $3,000, what is the net book value?

AS-22 (❺)

What is the purpose of a contra account?

AS-23 (❺)

True or False: All long-term assets are depreciated.

AS-24 (❺)

What is the residual value of an asset?

Application Questions

AP-1 (❶, ❷)

Match each of the following balance sheet accounts to the appropriate description in the table below.

- Prepaid Expense
- Unearned Revenue
- Accounts Receivable
- Office Supplies
- Cash

Term (fill in)	**Account Description**
	Fill in the blank: When a customer pays *immediately* for services provided, the service provider's revenue increases and _______ increases.
	Cash, and this account, are impacted when a company pays for expenses in advance.
	An example of prepaid expenses
	Cash, and this account, are impacted when a service company's customer pays *before* the service is delivered.
	Cash, and this account, are impacted when a service company's customer pays *after* the service is delivered.

AP-2 (❶, ❷)

Melbourne Consulting Company had the following transactions during the month of April 2011:

Date	Description
April 1	Earned $2,000 in cash for services provided
April 2	Paid $2,400 in advance for insurance coverage up to March 31, 2012
April 3	Charged $3,000 on account to customers for services performed
April 15	Customer paid $800 for a service delivered last month.
April 28	Incurred maintenance expense of $350, to be paid next month

Complete the following chart to account for the above transactions. Under the 'Account Type' column, fill the cells with one of the following: Asset, Liability, Revenue or Expense. The first transaction has been completed for you as an example.

Date	Account Name	Account Type	Increase or Decrease	Amount
April 1	Cash	Asset	Increase	$2,000
	Service Revenue	Revenue	Increase	$2,000
April 2				
April 3				
April 15				
April 28				

AP-3 (➊, ➋)

GGY Service Company has a monthly accounting period. GGY had the following transactions during the month of May 2011:

Date	Description
May 1	Paid $2,000 in cash for travel expenses incurred on this day
May 2	Paid $1,000 in advance for maintenance services to be provided next month
May 18	Received a prepayment of $1,500 from a customer for services to be provided in two months.
May 25	Paid $750 for a service that was provided to GGY three months ago
May 30	Incurred repairs expense of $1,000, which was paid for two months ago

Complete the following chart to account for the above transactions. Under the 'Account Type' column, fill the cells with one of the following: Asset, Liability, Revenue or Expense.

Date	Account Name	Account Type	Increase or Decrease	Amount
May 1				
May 2				
May 18				
May 25				
May 30				

AP-4 (➊)

Gwen Lawn Company (GLC) is a lawn maintenance company. On January 1, 2010, one of its customers paid $12,000 in cash to GLC for lawn care services to be provided over the course of the year (until December 31, 2010). The amount of work GLC will do for the customer will be spread evenly throughout the year. The company has a monthly accounting period.

On January 1, 2010, GLC recorded the following incorrect entry to account for the $12,000 payment:

- Increase cash (asset) by $12,000
- Increase revenue (income statement) by $12,000

By how much has GLC overstated or understated revenue in January 2010?

AP-5 (➊)

Halton & Mauler LLP is a successful corporate law firm. On January 1, 2010, one of its clients paid $16,800 in cash to Halton & Mauler for legal services to be provided over the course of the year (until December 31, 2010). The amount of work the company will do for the client will be spread evenly throughout the year. The law firm produces financial statements on a monthly basis.

On January 1, 2010, Halton & Mauler recorded the following incorrect entry to account for the $16,800 payment:

- Increase cash (asset) by $16,800
- Increase revenue (income statement) by $16,800

By how much has Halton & Mauler overstated or understated revenue for each month in 2010?

AP-6 (➊, ➋)

MYK Service Company has a monthly accounting period. MYK had the following transactions during the month of June 2011:

Date	Description
June 3	Paid $1,200 in cash for maintenance expenses incurred on this day
June 4	Paid $950 in advance for services to be provided next month
June 7	Received a prepayment of $1,100 from a customer for services to be provided in one month
June 10	Paid $400 for a service that was provided to MYK two months ago
June 15	Incurred rent expense of $4,000, which was paid for two months ago
June 17	Earned $1,900 in cash for services provided

June 18	Paid $2,400 in advance for one year insurance coverage
June 23	Charged $500 on account to customers for services performed
June 26	Customer paid $400 for a service provided last month
June 30	Purchased supplies for $650, to be paid next month

Complete the following chart to account for the above transactions.

Date	Account Name	Increase or Decrease	Amount
June 3			
June 4			
June 7			
June 10			
June 15			
June 17			
June 18			
June 23			
June 26			
June 30			

AP-7 (❶, ❷)

Place a checkmark beside each transaction that affects owner's equity.

Transaction	Affects Owner's Equity? (Place Checkmark)
Made a prepayment for services to be provided in six months	
Made an adjustment to recognize a prepaid expense in the income statement	
Made an adjustment to recognize unearned revenue in the income statement	
Received a payment from a customer for services to be provided in three months	
Performed a service and received cash as payment	
Performed a service, to be paid for by the customer in two months	

AP-8 (❸, ❹)

Which one of the following scenarios will require an adjustment? Place a checkmark beside each one that applies.

Scenario	Requires future adjustment?
Customer makes a prepayment to company for services to be provided in the future	
Company makes prepayment to a supplier for goods to be delivered in the future	
Company provides a service and receives cash for it immediately	
Company purchases property, plant & equipment	
Company borrows a three-year interest bearing bond. The entire principal and interest amount is payable at maturity.	
Company makes cash payment for current month's rent	

AP-9 (❶, ❷, ❹)

ABC Service Company has a monthly accounting period. ABC had the following transactions during its first month of operations, May 2011:

Transaction #	Date	Description
1	May 2	The owner deposited $50,000 cash into the business
2	May 4	Paid $10,000 in cash for property, plant & equipment
3	May 5	Paid $1,500 in cash for travel expenses incurred on this day
4	May 8	Paid $1,000 in advance for maintenance services to be provided next month
5	May 15	Received $9,000 cash for services provided
6	May 18	Received a prepayment of $1,300 from a customer for services to be provided in three months.
7	May 30	Paid $1,000 for May's rent expense
8	May 31	Recorded depreciation of $400

Required:

Complete the T-Account worksheet for May 2011.

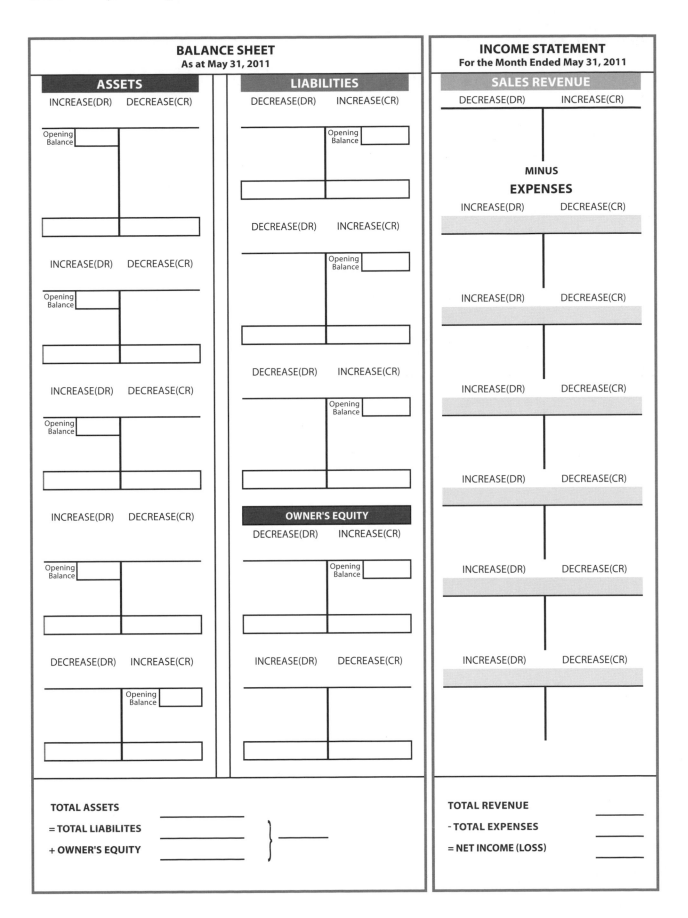

BALANCE SHEET
As at May 31, 2011

ASSETS

INCREASE(DR) DECREASE(CR)
Opening Balance

INCREASE(DR) DECREASE(CR)
Opening Balance

INCREASE(DR) DECREASE(CR)
Opening Balance

INCREASE(DR) DECREASE(CR)
Opening Balance

DECREASE(DR) INCREASE(CR)
Opening Balance

LIABILITIES

DECREASE(DR) INCREASE(CR)
Opening Balance

DECREASE(DR) INCREASE(CR)
Opening Balance

DECREASE(DR) INCREASE(CR)
Opening Balance

OWNER'S EQUITY

DECREASE(DR) INCREASE(CR)
Opening Balance

INCREASE(DR) DECREASE(CR)

TOTAL ASSETS ______

= TOTAL LIABILITES ______

+ OWNER'S EQUITY ______ } ______

INCOME STATEMENT
For the Month Ended May 31, 2011

SALES REVENUE

DECREASE(DR) INCREASE(CR)

MINUS

EXPENSES

INCREASE(DR) DECREASE(CR)

INCREASE(DR) DECREASE(CR)

INCREASE(DR) DECREASE(CR)

INCREASE(DR) DECREASE(CR)

INCREASE(DR) DECREASE(CR)

INCREASE(DR) DECREASE(CR)

TOTAL REVENUE ______

- TOTAL EXPENSES ______

= NET INCOME (LOSS) ______

AP-10 (❶, ❷, ❹)

DEFG Consulting Company has a monthly accounting period. DEFG had the following transactions during its first month of operations, June 2011:

Transaction #	Date	Description
1	June 5	The owner deposited $100,000 cash into the business
2	June 10	Paid $30,000 in cash for property, plant & equipment
3	June 14	Sold $12,000 worth of services to a customer (paid on account)
4	June 20	Paid $2,000 cash for June's rent
5	June 26	Received $3,000 in cash for consulting services to be provided in two months
6	June 30	Paid $6,000 in salaries for June
7	June 30	Accrued interest expense of $1,400
8	June 30	Recorded depreciation of $100

Required:

Complete the T-Account worksheet for June 2011.

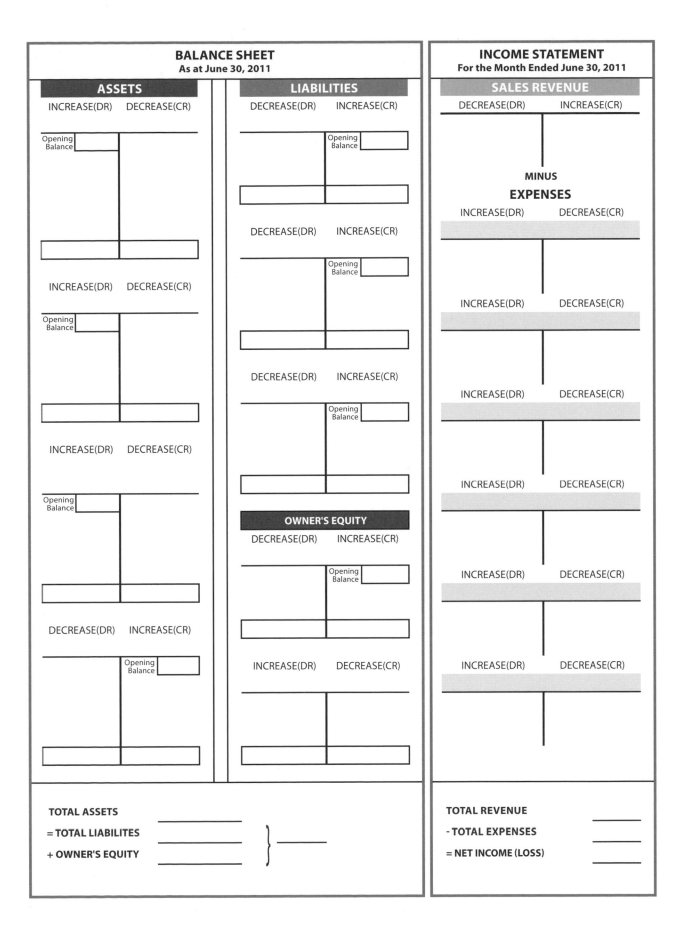

BALANCE SHEET
As at June 30, 2011

ASSETS

INCREASE(DR) DECREASE(CR)

Opening Balance

INCREASE(DR) DECREASE(CR)

Opening Balance

INCREASE(DR) DECREASE(CR)

Opening Balance

DECREASE(DR) INCREASE(CR)

Opening Balance

LIABILITIES

DECREASE(DR) INCREASE(CR)

Opening Balance

DECREASE(DR) INCREASE(CR)

Opening Balance

DECREASE(DR) INCREASE(CR)

Opening Balance

OWNER'S EQUITY

DECREASE(DR) INCREASE(CR)

Opening Balance

INCREASE(DR) DECREASE(CR)

TOTAL ASSETS ______

= TOTAL LIABILITES ______

+ OWNER'S EQUITY ______ } ______

INCOME STATEMENT
For the Month Ended June 30, 2011

SALES REVENUE

DECREASE(DR) INCREASE(CR)

MINUS

EXPENSES

INCREASE(DR) DECREASE(CR)

INCREASE(DR) DECREASE(CR)

INCREASE(DR) DECREASE(CR)

INCREASE(DR) DECREASE(CR)

INCREASE(DR) DECREASE(CR)

INCREASE(DR) DECREASE(CR)

TOTAL REVENUE ______

- TOTAL EXPENSES ______

= NET INCOME (LOSS) ______

AP –11 (❶, ❷, ❹)

Alton Safety Company has a monthly accounting period. The following are the company's account balances as at June 1, 2011:

Assets	**Liabilities**
Cash: $40,000	Accounts Payable: $30,000
Accounts Receivable: $21,000	Unearned Revenue: $3,600
Prepaid Rent: $4,800	Loans Payable: $60,000
Property, Plant & Equipment: $50,000	**Owner's Equity**
Accumulated Depreciation: ($5,000)	Capital Account: $17,200

Consider the following financial information as well:

- On May 31st, the company paid $4,800 as three months of rent in advance to Stratford Grant Properties (for June, July and August)
- On May 31st, Customer A made a deposit of $3,600 for services to be offered over the course of the next three months evenly

Alton Safety Company had the following transactions during June 2011:

Transaction #	Date	Description
1	June 1	The owner deposited an additional $40,000 cash into the business
2	June 10	Paid $30,000 in cash to purchase property, plant & equipment
3	June 15	Paid $1,200 cash for travel expense
4	June 20	Sold $15,000 worth of services on account
5	June 21	Collected $10,000 cash from a customer who owed money
6	June 30	Recognized rent expense for June (prepaid to Stratford Grant Properties in previous month)
7	June 30	Recognized June's revenue related to payment by Customer A on May 31st
8	June 30	Paid $6,000 for June's salaries

Required:

Complete the T-Account worksheet for June 2011.

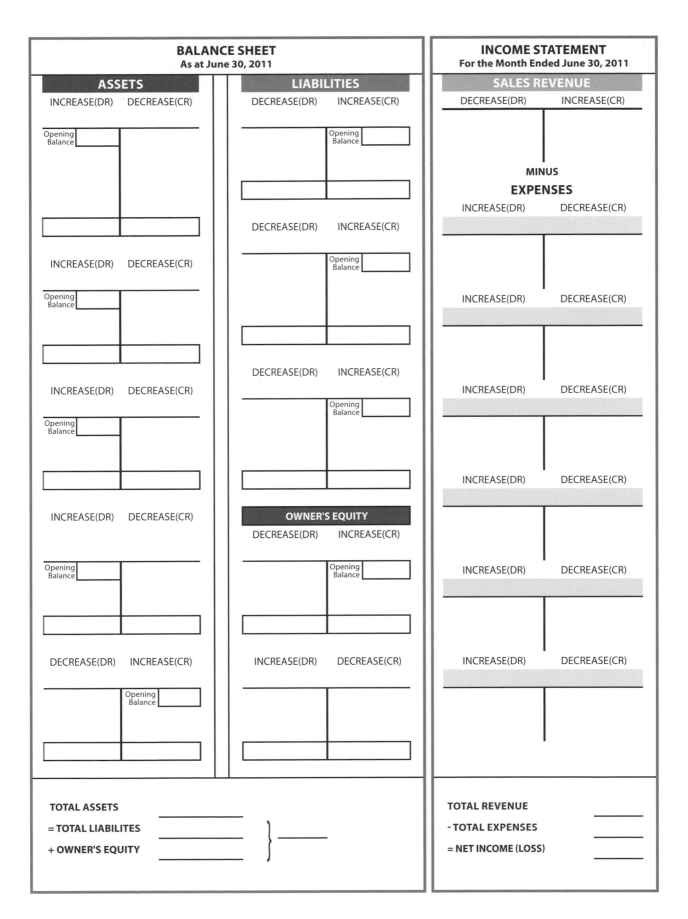

BALANCE SHEET
As at June 30, 2011

ASSETS

INCREASE(DR) DECREASE(CR)

Opening Balance

INCREASE(DR) DECREASE(CR)

Opening Balance

INCREASE(DR) DECREASE(CR)

Opening Balance

INCREASE(DR) DECREASE(CR)

Opening Balance

DECREASE(DR) INCREASE(CR)

Opening Balance

LIABILITIES

DECREASE(DR) INCREASE(CR)

Opening Balance

DECREASE(DR) INCREASE(CR)

Opening Balance

DECREASE(DR) INCREASE(CR)

Opening Balance

OWNER'S EQUITY

DECREASE(DR) INCREASE(CR)

Opening Balance

INCREASE(DR) DECREASE(CR)

TOTAL ASSETS ______

= TOTAL LIABILITES ______

+ OWNER'S EQUITY ______ } ______

INCOME STATEMENT
For the Month Ended June 30, 2011

SALES REVENUE

DECREASE(DR) INCREASE(CR)

MINUS

EXPENSES

INCREASE(DR) DECREASE(CR)

INCREASE(DR) DECREASE(CR)

INCREASE(DR) DECREASE(CR)

INCREASE(DR) DECREASE(CR)

INCREASE(DR) DECREASE(CR)

INCREASE(DR) DECREASE(CR)

TOTAL REVENUE ______

- TOTAL EXPENSES ______

= NET INCOME (LOSS) ______

AP-12 (❹)

Cherry Consulting purchased a new photocopier for $6,000 on January 1, 2011. The photocopier has a useful life of three years. After three years, the photocopier will be disposed of and will not have a residual value.

Complete the table to record the depreciation expense, accumulated depreciation and book value for the three years.

Year	Original Cost of PPE	Depreciation Expense	Accumulated Depreciation	Book Value
0	$6,000	$0	$0	$6,000
Total				

AP-13 (❹)

Hans Trucking purchased a new truck for $90,000 on January 1, 2011. The truck has a useful life of five years. After five years, the truck will be disposed of and will have a residual value of $1,000.

Complete the table to record the depreciation expense, accumulated depreciation and book value for the five years.

Year	Original Cost of PPE	Depreciation Expense	Accumulated Depreciation	Book Value
0	$90,000	$0	$0	$90,000
Total				

Chapter 5

BUSINESS ACCOUNTING CYCLE PART I

Assessment Questions

AS-1 (➊)

What does the term debit refer to?

____

____

AS-2 (➊)

True or False: A credit will always be an increase to any account.

____

____

AS-3 (➊)

Which three types of accounts use the debit side of the T-Account to increase their value?

____

____

AS-4 (➊)

Which three types of accounts use the credit side of the T-Account to increase their value?

____

____

AS-5 (➊)

What is the normal balance of an asset?

____

____

AS-6 (❶)

What is the normal balance of a liability?

AS-7 (❷)

Explain the purpose of a chart of accounts.

AS-8 (❷)

What are the six steps of the accounting cycle?

AS-9 (❷)

In the accounting cycle, what is the purpose of creating journals?

AS-10 (❸)

In the accounting cycle, what is the purpose of the general ledger?

AS-11 (❹)

In the accounting cycle, what is the purpose of the trial balance?

____

____

____

AS-12 (❷)

In the journal, what information will be entered in the PR (posting reference) column?

____

____

____

AS-13 (❸)

What is the relationship between the closing balance and the opening balance for an asset?

____

____

____

AS-14 (❹)

If the trial balance balances, were all transactions correctly recorded? Explain.

____

____

____

Application Questions

AP-1 (❶)

For the following list of accounts, indicate which side of the T-Account causes an increase or decrease. The first account has been done for you.

Account	Debit	Credit
Cash	Increase	Decrease
Advertising Expense		
Service Revenue		
Unearned Revenue		
Accounts Receivable		
Accounts Payable		
Capital Account		
Owner's Drawings		
Prepaid Rent		
Rent Expense		

AP-2 (❶)

For the accounts listed below, determine if the normal balance is a debit or a credit. Also, indicate if a debit or a credit will be needed to increase and decrease the account balance.

	Account Title	Normal Balance	Increase	Decrease
1	Cash			
2	Accounts Receivable			
3	Accounts Payable			
4	Loan Payable			
5	Capital Account			
6	Service Revenue			
7	Insurance Expense			
8	Prepaid Insurance			
9	Interest Receivable			
10	Property, Plant & Equipment			
11	Unearned Revenue			
12	Rent Revenue			
13	Owner's Drawings			
14	Salaries and Wages Expense			
15	Office Supplies			

AP-3 (❶)

The following are the accounts of Micro Company and their corresponding normal balances on May 31, 2011:

Account Titles	Balance
Capital Account	$23,500
Insurance Expense	900
Accounts Payable	15,500
Service Revenue	8,900
Property, Plant & Equipment	34,500
Supplies Expense	3,000
Cash	6,400
Salaries Expense	4,000
Rent Expense	3,000
Owner's Drawings	3,000
Utilities Expense	1,300
Bank Loan	10,200
Prepaid Insurance	2,000

Required:

Prepare Micro Company's trial balance for the month ended May 31, 2011.

Micro Company Trial Balance May 31, 2011		
ACCOUNT TITLES	**DEBIT**	**CREDIT**
Total		

AP-4 (➊)

Esteem Fitness provides fitness services for its customers. During the current month, Esteem Fitness had the following transactions:

1) Sold one month memberships to customers for $4,500 on account.
2) Received a telephone bill for $250 which will be paid next month.
3) Paid an employee's salary of $1,200.
4) Received $3,000 cash from customers paying for an upcoming one-year membership.
5) Paid $6,000 cash for six months of rent (the six months are upcoming).
6) Received a $10,000 loan from the bank.
7) Purchased new equipment with $8,000 cash.

Record each transaction in the table shown below.

	Account Name	Increase or Decrease	Debit	Credit
1				
2				
3				
4				
5				
6				
7				

AP-5 (➊)

Have-a-Bash provides party planning services. During the current month, Have-a-Bash had the following transactions.

1) The owner invested $5,000 cash into the business.
2) Planned a party for a customer and received $900 cash.
3) Received a $500 utilities bill which will be paid later.
4) Paid $50 interest on a bank loan.
5) Paid $400 towards the bank loan principal.
6) Received cash from a customer who owed $1,100.
7) Paid the utilities bill received earlier.

Record each transaction in the table.

	Account Name	Increase or Decrease	Debit	Credit
1				
2				
3				
4				
5				
6				
7				

AP-6 (❷)

Kick-off Sports Training helps train children in various sporting activities. During May 2011, the following transactions took place.

May 3	Received maintenance bill - to be paid next month	$500
May 3	Received cash for services provided	$2,750
May 4	Borrowed cash from the bank	$4,000
May 4	Received interest on company savings account	$220
May 10	Prepaid insurance for one year	$1,200
May 10	Paid telephone expenses for the month with cash	$150
May 11	Paid cash to reduce the balance of accounts payable	$700
May 15	Paid interest on bank loan	$25

Prepare the journal entries for the above transactions.

Date	Account Title and Explanation	Debit	Credit

AP-7 (❷)

Rejuvenation Spa provides a relaxing retreat for people wishing to relax and unwind. During the month of July 2011, the following transactions took place:

July 3	Provided services to a customer on account	$3,600
July 4	Borrowed cash from the bank	$2,000
July 6	Provides services to a customer and received cash	$2,400
July 10	Received the telephone bill, which will be paid later	$250
July 11	Paid cash to reduce the balance of accounts payable	$600
July 15	Collected cash from customers owing on account	$1,800
July 20	Paid the telephone bill from July 10	$250
July 21	Paid a portion of bank loan principal	$1,500
July 31	Paid salaries for the month with cash	$1,600
July 31	Purchased equipment – to be paid later	$1,900

Prepare the journal entries for the above transactions.

Date	Account Title and Explanation	Debit	Credit

AP-8 (❷)

Noel Dy opened an automobile repair shop. The following are the transactions that occurred during the month of March 2011:

Mar 1	Noel Dy invested $10,000 cash and $8,000 worth of equipment in the business
Mar 3	Paid $1,000 cash to rent the shop space
Mar 5	Purchased $1,200 worth of shop tools using cash
Mar 7	Received $2,000 cash for repair work done for MJ Gonzales
Mar 8	Purchased additional shop tools from Adrian Cruz worth $1,000, on account
Mar 15	Paid half of the amount due to Adrian Cruz with cash
Mar 18	Paid $200 cash to local publication for advertising
Mar 19	Paid $1,000 of salaries to shop helpers with cash
Mar 20	Noel Dy withdrew $1,500 cash for personal use
Mar 29	Bought $1,000 worth of chairs and tables for the shop on account
Mar 31	Invested additional equipment worth $5,000 for business use
Mar 31	Received $3,000 cash from various customers for repairs done on their automobiles

Noel Dy's bookkeeper established the following chart of accounts:

Account Description	Account #
ASSETS	
Cash	101
Accounts Receivable	105
Prepaid Insurance	110
Shop Tools	115
Property, Plant & Equipment	120
Accumulated Depreciation	125
LIABILITIES	
Accounts Payable	200
Interest Payable	205
Unearned Revenue	210
Bank Loan	215
OWNER'S EQUITY	
Capital Account	300
Owner's Drawings	310
Income Summary	315

Account Description	Account #
REVENUE	
Service Revenue	400
Interest Earned on Savings	410
EXPENSES	
Advertising Expense	500
Bad Debt Expense	505
Depreciation Expense	510
Insurance Expense	515
Interest Expense	520
Maintenance Expense	525
Office Supplies Expense	530
Professional Fees Expense	535
Rent Expense	540
Salaries Expense	545
Telephone Expense	550
Travel Expense	555

Required:

Using the given general journal, prepare journal entries for the above transactions.

Journal

Date	Account Title and Explanation	PR	Debit	Credit

Date	Account Title and Explanation	PR	Debit	Credit

AP-9 (❷, ❸, ❹)

Thomas Topology provides surveying services to construction companies and municipalities. The closing balance at the end of March 2011 and their chart of accounts is shown below.

Thomas Topology Balance Sheet As at March 31, 2011			
Assets		**Liabilities**	
Cash	$22,000	Accounts Payable	$10,500
Accounts Receivable	9,000	Unearned Revenue	4,500
Property, Plant & Equipment	8,000	Bank Loan	6,000
		Total Liabilities	21,000
		Owners' Equity	18,000
Total Assets	$39,000	**Total Liabilities & Owners' Equity**	$39,000

Account Description	Account #
ASSETS	
Cash	101
Accounts Receivable	105
Prepaid Insurance	110
Office Supplies	115
Property, Plant & Equipment	120
Accumulated Depreciation	125
LIABILITIES	
Accounts Payable	200
Interest Payable	205
Unearned Revenue	210
Bank Loan	215
OWNER'S EQUITY	
Capital Account	300
Owner's Drawings	310
Income Summary	315

Account Description	Account #
REVENUE	
Service Revenue	400
Interest Earned on Savings	410
EXPENSES	
Advertising Expense	500
Bad Debt Expense	505
Depreciation Expense	510
Insurance Expense	515
Interest Expense	520
Maintenance Expense	525
Office Supplies Expense	530
Professional Fees Expense	535
Rent Expense	540
Salaries Expense	545
Telephone Expense	550
Travel Expense	555

During the month of April, Thomas Topology had the following transactions:

Apr 1	Purchased office equipment on account	$7,000
Apr 2	Received cash for services provided	$25,000
Apr 3	Paid cash for April's rent	$1,000
Apr 4	Prepaid insurance for one year	$1,200
Apr 10	Paid cash to reduce the balance of accounts payable	$200
Apr 14	Paid cash for employee's salaries	$8,000
Apr 20	Paid interest on bank loan	$50
Apr 22	Received telephone bill which will be paid next month	$250
Apr 24	Recorded travel expenses to be paid next month	$8,000
Apr 30	Paid portion of bank loan	$4,500

Required:

1) Prepare the journal entries for the month of April.
2) Post the journal entries to the ledger accounts.
3) Prepare a trial balance at the end of April.

Journal **Page 1**

Date	Account Title and Explanation	PR	Debit	Credit

Account: Cash					**GL No:**	
Date	**Description**	**PR**	**DR**	**CR**	**Balance**	

Account:					**GL No:**	
Date	**Description**	**PR**	**DR**	**CR**	**Balance**	

Account:					**GL No:**	
Date	**Description**	**PR**	**DR**	**CR**	**Balance**	

Account:					**GL No:**	
Date	**Description**	**PR**	**DR**	**CR**	**Balance**	

Account:					**GL No:**	
Date	**Description**	**PR**	**DR**	**CR**	**Balance**	

Account:					**GL No:**	
Date	**Description**	**PR**	**DR**	**CR**	**Balance**	

Account:					**GL No:**	
Date	**Description**	**PR**	**DR**	**CR**	**Balance**	

Account:					**GL No:**	
Date	**Description**	**PR**	**DR**	**CR**	**Balance**	

Account:					**GL No:**	
Date	**Description**	**PR**	**DR**	**CR**	**Balance**	

Account:					**GL No:**	
Date	**Description**	**PR**	**DR**	**CR**	**Balance**	

Account:					**GL No:**	
Date	**Description**	**PR**	**DR**	**CR**	**Balance**	

Account:					**GL No:**	
Date	**Description**	**PR**	**DR**	**CR**	**Balance**	

Account:					GL No:	
Date	Description	PR	DR	CR	Balance	

Account:					GL No:	
Date	Description	PR	DR	CR	Balance	

Thomas Topology Trial Balance April 30, 2011		
Account Titles	DR	CR

AP-10 (❷, ❸, ❹)

High Flying Biplane provides sight-seeing tours in vintage biplanes. The closing balance at the end of May 2011 and their chart of accounts is shown below.

High Flying Biplane Balance Sheet As at May 31, 2011			
Assets		**Liabilities**	
Cash	$8,000	Accounts Payable	$8,200
Accounts Receivable	6,000	Unearned Revenue	3,200
Prepaid Insurance	1,200	Bank Loan	20,000
Property, Plant & Equipment	60,000	**Total Liabilities**	31,400
		Owners' Equity	43,800
Total Assets	$75,200	**Total Liabilities & Owners' Equity**	$75,200

Account Description	Account #
ASSETS	
Cash	101
Accounts Receivable	105
Prepaid Insurance	110
Office Supplies	115
Property, Plant & Equipment	120
Accumulated Depreciation	125
LIABILITIES	
Accounts Payable	200
Interest Payable	205
Unearned Revenue	210
Bank Loan	215
OWNER'S EQUITY	
Capital Account	300
Owner's Drawings	310
Income Summary	315

Account Description	Account #
REVENUE	
Service Revenue	400
Interest Earned on Savings	410
EXPENSES	
Advertising Expense	500
Bad Debt Expense	505
Depreciation Expense	510
Insurance Expense	515
Interest Expense	520
Maintenance Expense	525
Office Supplies Expense	530
Professional Fees Expense	535
Rent Expense	540
Salaries Expense	545
Telephone Expense	550
Travel Expense	555

During the month of June, High Flying Biplane had the following transactions.

Jun 1	The owner invested cash into the business	$5,000
Jun 2	Received cash for tours that will be provided in August	$1,500
Jun 3	Received an advertising bill which will be paid next month	$400
Jun 4	Paid the telephone bill with cash	$200
Jun 10	Provided tours to customer who will pay later	$2,400
Jun 14	Purchase some equipment with cash	$4,000

Jun 20	Received payment from customers paying their account	$1,600
Jun 22	Paid part of accounts payable	$900
Jun 24	Paid bank loan principal	$1,000
Jun 30	The owner withdrew cash for personal use	$1,200

Required:

1) Prepare the journal entries for the month of June.
2) Post the journal entries to the ledger accounts.
3) Prepare a trial balance at the end of June.

Journal				**Page 1**
Date	**Account Title and Explanation**	**PR**	**Debit**	**Credit**

Date	Account Title and Explanation	PR	Debit	Credit

Account: Cash					GL No:	
Date	Description	PR	DR	CR	Balance	

Account:					GL No:	
Date	Description	PR	DR	CR	Balance	

Account:					**GL No:**	
Date	**Description**	**PR**	**DR**	**CR**	**Balance**	

Account:					**GL No:**	
Date	**Description**	**PR**	**DR**	**CR**	**Balance**	

Account:					**GL No:**	
Date	**Description**	**PR**	**DR**	**CR**	**Balance**	

Account:					**GL No:**	
Date	**Description**	**PR**	**DR**	**CR**	**Balance**	

Account:					**GL No:**	
Date	**Description**	**PR**	**DR**	**CR**	**Balance**	

Account:					GL No:	
Date	Description	PR	DR	CR	Balance	

Account:					GL No:	
Date	Description	PR	DR	CR	Balance	

Account:					GL No:	
Date	Description	PR	DR	CR	Balance	

Account:					GL No:	
Date	Description	PR	DR	CR	Balance	

Account:					GL No:	
Date	Description	PR	DR	CR	Balance	

High Flying Biplane Trial Balance June 30, 2011		
Account Titles	**DR**	**CR**

AP-11 (❷, ❸, ❹)

Limbo Lower provides acrobatic entertainment at children's parties and other events. The closing balance at the end of August 2011 and their chart of accounts is shown below.

Limbo Lower Balance Sheet As at August 31, 2011			
Assets		**Liabilities**	
Cash	$7,200	Accounts Payable	$3,400
Accounts Receivable	2,300	Unearned Revenue	1,400
Office Supplies	850	Bank Loan	5,600
Property, Plant & Equipment	11,500	**Total Liabilities**	10,400
		Owners' Equity	11,450
Total Assets	$21,850	**Total Liabilities & Owners' Equity**	$21,850

Account Description	Account #
ASSETS	
Cash	101
Accounts Receivable	105
Prepaid Insurance	110
Office Supplies	115
Property, Plant & Equipment	120
Accumulated Depreciation	125
LIABILITIES	
Accounts Payable	200
Interest Payable	205
Unearned Revenue	210
Bank Loan	215
OWNER'S EQUITY	
Capital Account	300
Owner's Drawings	310
Income Summary	315

Account Description	Account #
REVENUE	
Service Revenue	400
Interest Earned on Savings	410
EXPENSES	
Advertising Expense	500
Bad Debt Expense	505
Depreciation Expense	510
Insurance Expense	515
Interest Expense	520
Maintenance Expense	525
Office Supplies Expense	530
Professional Fees Expense	535
Rent Expense	540
Salaries Expense	545
Telephone Expense	550
Travel Expense	555

During the month of September, Limbo Lower had the following transactions.

Sep 1	Paid cash in advance for a one year insurance policy	$1,800
Sep 2	Received cash for services provided	$1,900
Sep 3	Paid cash for September's rent	$1,350
Sep 4	Purchased office supplies on account	$250
Sep 10	Paid interest on bank loan	$40
Sep 10	Paid bank loan principal	$960
Sep 20	Sold some equipment for its book value and received cash	$2,200
Sep 22	Received payment from customer paying their account	$850
Sep 24	Paid a portion of accounts payable	$600
Sep 30	The owner withdrew cash for personal use	$1,600

Required:

1) Prepare the journal entries for the month of September.
2) Post the journal entries to the ledger accounts.
3) Prepare a trial balance at the end of September.

Journal				Page 1
Date	**Account Title and Explanation**	**PR**	**Debit**	**Credit**

Account: Cash					GL No:	
Date	Description	PR	DR	CR	Balance	

Account:					GL No:	
Date	Description	PR	DR	CR	Balance	

Account:					GL No:	
Date	Description	PR	DR	CR	Balance	

Account:					GL No:	
Date	Description	PR	DR	CR	Balance	

Account:					GL No:	
Date	Description	PR	DR	CR	Balance	

Account:					GL No:	
Date	**Description**	**PR**	**DR**	**CR**	**Balance**	

Account:					GL No:	
Date	**Description**	**PR**	**DR**	**CR**	**Balance**	

Account:					GL No:	
Date	**Description**	**PR**	**DR**	**CR**	**Balance**	

Account:					GL No:	
Date	**Description**	**PR**	**DR**	**CR**	**Balance**	

Account:					GL No:	
Date	**Description**	**PR**	**DR**	**CR**	**Balance**	

Account:					GL No:	
Date	Description	PR	DR	CR	Balance	

Account:					GL No:	
Date	Description	PR	DR	CR	Balance	

Account:					GL No:	
Date	Description	PR	DR	CR	Balance	

Limbo Lower
Trial Balance
September 30, 2011

Account Titles	DR	CR

AP-12 (❶, ❹)

A part-time bookkeeper for Wombat Tours has created the trial balance at the end of the year and cannot get it to balance.

Wombat Tours Trial Balance December 31, 2011		
Account Titles	**DR**	**CR**
Accounts Payable	$3,150	
Accounts Receivable	2,350	
Advertising Expense		$2,100
Bank Loan		5,200
Capital Account		6,170
Cash	6,200	
Interest Expense	560	
Maintenance Expense	240	
Office Supplies		1,600
Owner's Drawings		2,300
Prepaid Insurance	1,200	
Property, Plant & Equipment	13,500	
Rent Expense	6,200	
Salaries Expense	5,300	
Service Revenue		25,800
Telephone Expense	450	
Unearned Revenue	1,680	
Total	$40,830	$43,170

All the entries have been journalized and posted to the general ledger properly, and all the accounts should have normal balances.

Re-create the trial balance for Wombat Tours so that the accounts are listed in the order they would typically appear in a chart of accounts, and ensure that debits will equal credits.

Note: All accounts have normal balances.

Wombat Tours Trial Balance December 31, 2011		
Account Titles	**DR**	**CR**

Chapter 6

BUSINESS ACCOUNTING CYCLE PART II

Assessment Questions

AS-1 (❶)

What is the purpose of a worksheet?

AS-2 (❶)

Why must adjustments be made at the end of the accounting period?

AS-3 (❶)

When making an adjustment to record unearned revenue that is now earned, which accounts are used and how are they affected?

AS-4 (❶)

When making an adjustment to record depreciation on property, plant and equipment, which accounts are used and how are they affected?

AS-5 (❶)

When making an adjustment to record the used portion of prepaid insurance, which accounts are used and how are they affected?

____

____

AS-6 (❶)

When making an adjustment to record accrued interest on a bank loan, which accounts are used and how are they affected?

____

____

AS-7 (❷)

What is an adjusted trial balance?

____

____

AS-8 (❸)

What does the income statement report?

____

____

AS-9 (❸)

Which statement is prepared after the income statement but before the balance sheet?

____

____

AS-10 (❸)

What does the statement of owner's equity report?

____

____

AS-11 (❸)

What two items will cause owner's equity to increase and what two items will cause owner's equity to decrease?

____

____

____

AS-12 (❸)

Which categories of accounts will be reported on the balance sheet?

____

____

AS-13 (❸)

How does accumulated depreciation affect the value of property, plant and equipment?

____

____

AS-14 (❺)

What does it mean to close the books?

____

____

____

AS-15 (❺)

What are the three steps to close directly to the capital account?

AS-16 (❺)

What are the four steps to close the accounts using the income summary?

AS-17 (❺)

If a company has a net income for the period and closes their books using the income summary account, will the income summary account have a debit or credit balance before it is closed to the capital account?

AS-18 (❺)

Which categories of accounts will appear on the post-closing trial balance?

AS-19 (❻)

Identify two benefits of a computerized accounting system.

Application Questions

AP-1 (❶, ❷)

Swordfish Programming provides computer solutions to the security industry. At the end of April 2011, they had the following adjustments:

1) A count of office supplies showed that there was $550 remaining in the office.
2) The balance of prepaid insurance is for a 12 month policy, one month of insurance has been used.
3) During April, Swordfish Programming earned $900 of unearned revenue.
4) Property, plant and equipment depreciated $120 during April.

Required:

Using the following trial balance, complete the adjustments and the adjusted trial balance in the worksheet.

Swordfish Programming Worksheet April 30, 2011						
	Unadjusted Trial Balance		Adjustments		Adjusted Trial Balance	
Account	**Debit**	**Credit**	**Debit**	**Credit**	**Debit**	**Credit**
Cash	$4,200					
Accounts Receivable	2,300					
Prepaid Insurance	1,800					
Office Supplies	800					
Property, Plant and Equipment	10,400					
Accumulated Depreciation		$0				
Accounts Payable		1,640				
Unearned Revenue		1,950				
Bank Loan		3,200				
Capital Account		11,035				
Owner's Drawings	1,500					
Service Revenue		4,750				
Depreciation Expense	0					
Insurance Expense	0					
Office Supplies Expense	0					
Rent Expense	1,300					
Telephone Expense	275					
Total	$22,575	$22,575				

AP-2 (❶, ❷)

Chirp Hearing provides hearing aids and other auditory services. At the end of November 2011, they had the following adjustments:

1) Accrued $40 interest on the bank loan.
2) The balance of the prepaid insurance is for the remaining 10 months of the insurance policy. One month of insurance has been used.
3) One month of depreciation is $180.
4) Chirp Hearing completed $650 of work that was previously unearned.
5) Office supplies used during the month totalled $400.

Required:

Using the following trial balance, complete the adjustments and the adjusted trial balance in the worksheet.

Chirp Hearing Worksheet November 30, 2011						
	Unadjusted Trial Balance		**Adjustments**		**Adjusted Trial Balance**	
Account	**Debit**	**Credit**	**Debit**	**Credit**	**Debit**	**Credit**
Cash	$6,250					
Accounts Receivable	3,440					
Prepaid Insurance	2,200					
Office Supplies	1,140					
Property, Plant and Equipment	15,400					
Accumulated Depreciation		$360				
Accounts Payable		2,260				
Interest Payable		0				
Unearned Revenue		1,240				
Bank Loan		4,500				
Capital Account		13,220				
Owner's Drawings	2,100					
Service Revenue		12,500				
Depreciation Expense	0					
Insurance Expense	0					
Interest Expense	0					
Office Supplies Expense	0					
Rent Expense	1,650					
Salaries Expense	1,900					
Total	$34,080	$34,080				

AP-3 (❶, ❷, ❸, ❹)

Mr. Allan Poe operates an advertising business called A Advertising. He had the following transactions for the month of December 2011:

Dec 2	Invested $25,000 cash in the business
Dec 5	Paid $2,500 cash for two months of rent in advance
Dec 5	Prepaid $600 cash for a one-year subscription to Manila Bulletin, a monthly trade magazine that is left in the office for visitors to read
Dec 8	Bought equipment worth $26,000 on account. The equipment has a useful life of 5 years with $2,000 salvage value
Dec 10	Received $6,000 cash as advertising income
Dec 11	Paid $13,000 cash as partial payment for the equipment bought on account
Dec 15	Paid $2,000 cash for salaries
Dec 27	Received $3,000 cash from Extreme Jockey Club for advertising services

Adjustments:

Dec 31	Recognized $1,250 rent expense for the month
Dec 31	One month of the annual subscription has been used. This will be expensed to office supplies expense
Dec 31	Depreciation for the month is $400

Chart of Accounts:

Account Description	Account #
ASSETS	
Cash	101
Accounts Receivable	105
Prepaid Rent	110
Prepaid Subscriptions	115
Property, Plant & Equipment	120
Accumulated Depreciation	125
LIABILITIES	
Accounts Payable	200
Interest Payable	205
Unearned Revenue	210
Bank Loan	215
OWNER'S EQUITY	
Capital Account	300
Owner's Drawings	310
Income Summary	315

Account Description	Account #
REVENUE	
Service Revenue	400
Interest Earned on Savings	410
EXPENSES	
Advertising Expense	500
Bad Debt Expense	505
Depreciation Expense	510
Insurance Expense	515
Interest Expense	520
Maintenance Expense	525
Office Supplies Expense	530
Professional Fees Expense	535
Rent Expense	540
Salaries Expense	545
Telephone Expense	550
Travel Expense	555

Required:

Prepare the journal entries, post them to the general ledger, and complete the trial balance worksheet.

Journal **Page 1**

Date	Account Title and Explanation	PR	Debit	Credit

Journal				Page 1
Date	**Account Title and Explanation**	**PR**	**Debit**	**Credit**

Account: Cash					GL. No.	
Date	**Description**	**PR**	**Debit**	**Credit**	**Balance**	

Account:					GL. No.	
Date	**Description**	**PR**	**Debit**	**Credit**	**Balance**	

Account:					GL. No.	
Date	**Description**	**PR**	**Debit**	**Credit**	**Balance**	

Account:					GL. No.	
Date	Description	PR	Debit	Credit	Balance	

Account:					GL. No.	
Date	Description	PR	Debit	Credit	Balance	

Account:					GL. No.	
Date	Description	PR	Debit	Credit	Balance	

Account:					GL. No.	
Date	Description	PR	Debit	Credit	Balance	

Account:					GL. No.	
Date	Description	PR	Debit	Credit	Balance	

Account:					**GL. No.**	
Date	**Description**	**PR**	**Debit**	**Credit**	**Balance**	

Account:					**GL. No.**	
Date	**Description**	**PR**	**Debit**	**Credit**	**Balance**	

Account:					**GL. No.**	
Date	**Description**	**PR**	**Debit**	**Credit**	**Balance**	

Account:					**GL. No.**	
Date	**Description**	**PR**	**Debit**	**Credit**	**Balance**	

A ADVERTISING WORKSHEET DECEMBER 31, 2011										
	Unadjusted Trial Balance		Adjustments		Adjusted Trial Balance		Income Statement		Balance Sheet	
ACCOUNT TITLES	Debit	Credit	Debit	Credit	Debit	Credit	Debit	Credit	Debit	Credit

AP-4 (❶, ❷, ❸, ❹)

Following is the list of transactions of MJ Sandblasting for the first month of operations during April 2011.

Apr 1	Owner invested $30,000 cash in the business
Apr 1	Purchased sandblasting equipment from Delta Company for $12,000. Paid $8,000 as a down payment with cash, and the remaining balance is payable in 60 days. The expected life of the equipment is 5 years
Apr 2	Purchased a one year insurance policy, costing $3,600
Apr 5	Paid $3,000 cash for garage and office rent
Apr 8	Received $5,000 cash from Billed Server Realty Corp. and $3,500 from Angela Building Corp. for services provided
Apr 14	Paid $1,000 cash for utilities

Apr 20 Paid $2,500 for salaries to employees

Apr 25 Owner withdrew $2,000 cash for personal use

Adjustments:

Apr 30 Recognized $300 of insurance expense for the month

Apr 30 Depreciation for the month is $200

Chart of Accounts:

Account Description	Account #
ASSETS	
Cash	101
Accounts Receivable	105
Prepaid Insurance	110
Office Supplies	115
Property, Plant & Equipment	120
Accumulated Depreciation	125
LIABILITIES	
Accounts Payable	200
Interest Payable	205
Unearned Revenue	210
Bank Loan	215
OWNER'S EQUITY	
Capital Account	300
Owner's Drawings	310
Income Summary	315

Account Description	Account #
REVENUE	
Service Revenue	400
Interest Earned on Savings	410
EXPENSES	
Advertising Expense	500
Bad Debt Expense	505
Depreciation Expense	510
Insurance Expense	515
Interest Expense	520
Maintenance Expense	525
Office Supplies Expense	530
Professional Fees Expense	535
Rent Expense	540
Salaries Expense	545
Telephone Expense	550
Utilities Expense	555

Required:

Prepare the journal entries, post them to the general ledger, and complete the trial balance worksheet.

Journal				Page 1
Date	**Account Title and Explanation**	**PR**	**Debit**	**Credit**

Journal				Page 1
Date	**Account Title and Explanation**	**PR**	**Debit**	**Credit**

Account: Cash					GL. No.	
Date	**Description**	**PR**	**Debit**	**Credit**	**Balance**	

Account:					GL. No.	
Date	**Description**	**PR**	**Debit**	**Credit**	**Balance**	

Account:					GL. No.	
Date	**Description**	**PR**	**Debit**	**Credit**	**Balance**	

Account:					GL. No.	
Date	**Description**	**PR**	**Debit**	**Credit**	**Balance**	

Account:					GL. No.	
Date	**Description**	**PR**	**Debit**	**Credit**	**Balance**	

Account:					**GL. No.**	
Date	**Description**	**PR**	**Debit**	**Credit**	**Balance**	

Account:					**GL. No.**	
Date	**Description**	**PR**	**Debit**	**Credit**	**Balance**	

Account:					**GL. No.**	
Date	**Description**	**PR**	**Debit**	**Credit**	**Balance**	

Account:					**GL. No.**	
Date	**Description**	**PR**	**Debit**	**Credit**	**Balance**	

Account:					**GL. No.**	
Date	**Description**	**PR**	**Debit**	**Credit**	**Balance**	

Account:					GL. No.	
Date	**Description**	**PR**	**Debit**	**Credit**	**Balance**	

Account:					GL. No.	
Date	**Description**	**PR**	**Debit**	**Credit**	**Balance**	

Account:					GL. No.	
Date	**Description**	**PR**	**Debit**	**Credit**	**Balance**	

MU Sandblasting
Worksheet
April 30, 2011

	Unadjusted Trial Balance		Adjustments		Adjusted Trial Balance		Income Statement		Balance Sheet	
Accounts	**Debit**	**Credit**	**Debit**	**Credit**	**Debit**	**Credit**	**Debit**	**Credit**	**Debit**	**Credit**

AP-5 (❶, ❷, ❸, ❹)

Sprig Gardening Service provides seasonal gardening services. At the end of August 2011, the company must make the following adjustments:

1) Depreciation for their property, plant and equipment is $120.
2) Interest due on a bank loan is $50. It will be paid next month.
3) Accrued salary expense for an employee at the end of the month. The company owes the employee $450.
4) One month of prepaid insurance at $70 per month has been used.
5) A physical count of office supplies shows that $300 was used during August.
6) Sprig Gardening earned $670 that was previously unearned.

Required:

Prepare the adjusting journal entries. You are not required to fill in the PR column for this question.

Answers:

Journal				Page 1
Date	Account Title and Explanation	PR	Debit	Credit

AP-6 (❶, ❷, ❸, ❹, ❺, ❻)

Thomas Topology has completed all their journal entries for the month of April 2011 and posted them to the general ledger. Based on the ledger balances, an unadjusted trial balance has been prepared. Their chart of accounts and unadjusted trial balance are listed below.

Account Description	Account #
ASSETS	
Cash	101
Accounts Receivable	105
Prepaid Insurance	110
Office Supplies	115
Property, Plant & Equipment	120
Accumulated Depreciation	125
LIABILITIES	
Accounts Payable	200
Interest Payable	205
Unearned Revenue	210
Bank Loan	215
OWNER'S EQUITY	
Capital Account	300
Owner's Drawings	310
Income Summary	315

Account Description	Account #
REVENUE	
Service Revenue	400
Interest Earned on Savings	410
EXPENSES	
Advertising Expense	500
Bad Debt Expense	505
Depreciation Expense	510
Insurance Expense	515
Interest Expense	520
Maintenance Expense	525
Office Supplies Expense	530
Professional Fees Expense	535
Rent Expense	540
Salaries Expense	545
Telephone Expense	550
Travel Expense	555

Thomas Topology
Unadjusted Trial Balance
April 30, 2010

Account Titles	DR	CR
Cash	$32,050	
Accounts Receivable	9,000	
Prepaid Insurance	1,200	
Property, Plant & Equipment	15,000	
Accounts Payable		$25,550
Unearned Revenue		4,500
Bank Loan		1,500
Capital Account		18,000
Service Revenue		25,000
Interest Expense	50	
Rent Expense	1,000	
Salaries Expense	8,000	
Telephone Expense	250	
Travel Expense	8,000	
Total	$74,550	$74,550

The following adjustments must be made at the end of April:

Apr 30	One month of prepaid insurance has been used	$100
Apr 30	Depreciation on property, plant and equipment	$120
Apr 30	Unearned revenue that has now been earned	$1,300

Required:

1) Fill in the unadjusted trial balance on the worksheet and complete the rest of the worksheet.
2) Prepare the income statement, statement of owner's equity and the balance sheet.
3) Create the journal entries for the adjustments from the worksheet and post the adjustments to the ledger accounts.
4) Create the closing entries using the income summary account and post the closing entries to the ledger accounts.
5) Prepare the post-closing trial balance.

Note: The daily transactions for the month of April have already been posted in the general ledger. You are only responsible for posting the adjusting and closing entries.

1) Worksheet

Thomas Topology
Worksheet
April 30, 2011

Account Titles	Unadjusted Trial Balance		Adjustments		Adjusted Trial Balance		Income Statement		Balance Sheet	
	Debit	Credit	Debit	Credit	Debit	Credit	Debit	Credit	Debit	Credit

2) Financial Statements

Thomas Topology Income Statement For the Month Ended April 30, 2011		

Thomas Topology Statement of Owner's Equity For the Month Ended April 30, 2011		

Thomas Topology Balance Sheet As at April 30, 2011		

3) Adjusting entries (the general ledger is at the end of this question).

Journal				**Page 2**
Date	**Account Title and Explanation**	**PR**	**DR**	**CR**

4) Closing entries (the general ledger is at the end of this question).

Journal				**Page 3**
Date	**Account Title and Explanation**	**PR**	**DR**	**CR**

5) Post-closing trial balance.

Thomas Topology Post-Closing Trial Balance April 30, 2011		
Account Titles	**DR**	**CR**

General Ledger

Account: Cash					GL. No: 101	
Date	**Description**	**PR**	**DR**	**CR**	**Balance**	
2011						
Apr 1	Opening Balance				22,000	DR
Apr 2		J1	25,000		47,000	DR
Apr 3		J1		1,000	46,000	DR
Apr 4		J1		1,200	44,800	DR
Apr 10		J1		200	44,600	DR
Apr 14		J1		8,000	36,600	DR
Apr 20		J1		50	36,550	DR
Apr 30		J1		4,500	32,050	DR

Account: Accounts Receivable					GL No: 105	
Date	**Description**	**PR**	**DR**	**CR**	**Balance**	
2011						
Apr 1	Opening Balance				9,000	DR

Account:	Prepaid Insurance				GL No: 110	
Date	**Description**	**PR**	**DR**	**CR**	**Balance**	
2011						
Apr 1	Opening Balance				0	DR
Apr 4		J1	1,200		1,200	DR

Account:	Property, Plant & Equipment				GL No: 120	
Date	**Description**	**PR**	**DR**	**CR**	**Balance**	
2011						
Apr 1	Opening Balance				8,000	DR
Apr 1		J1	7,000		15,000	DR

Account:	Accumulated Depreciation				GL No: 125	
Date	**Description**	**PR**	**DR**	**CR**	**Balance**	

Account:	Accounts Payable				GL No: 200	
Date	**Description**	**PR**	**DR**	**CR**	**Balance**	
2011						
Apr 1	Opening Balance				10,500	CR
Apr 1		J1		7,000	17,500	CR
Apr 10		J1	200		17,300	CR
Apr 22		J1		250	17,550	CR
Apr 24		J1		8,000	25,550	CR

Account:	Unearned Revenue				GL No: 210	
Date	**Description**	**PR**	**DR**	**CR**	**Balance**	
2011						
Apr 1	Opening Balance				4,500	CR

Account:	Bank Loan				GL No: 215	
Date	**Description**	**PR**	**DR**	**CR**	**Balance**	
2011						
Apr 1	Opening Balance				6,000	CR
Apr 30		J1	4,500		1,500	CR

Account:	Capital Account				GL No: 300	
Date	**Description**	**PR**	**DR**	**CR**	**Balance**	
2011						
Apr 1	Opening Balance				18,000	CR

Account:	Income Summary				GL No: 315	
Date	**Description**	**PR**	**DR**	**CR**	**Balance**	

Account:	Service Revenue				GL No: 400	
Date	**Description**	**PR**	**DR**	**CR**	**Balance**	
2011						
Apr 2		J1		25,000	25,000	CR

Account:	Depreciation Expense				GL No: 510	
Date	**Description**	**PR**	**DR**	**CR**	**Balance**	

Account:	Insurance Expense				GL No: 515	
Date	Description	PR	DR	CR	Balance	

Account:	Interest Expense				GL No: 520	
Date	Description	PR	DR	CR	Balance	
2011						
Apr 20		J1	50		50	DR

Account:	Rent Expense				GL No: 540	
Date	Description	PR	DR	CR	Balance	
2011						
Apr 3		J1	1,000		1,000	DR

Account:	Salaries Expense				GL No: 545	
Date	Description	PR	DR	CR	Balance	
2011						
Apr 14		J1	8,000		8,000	DR

Account:	Telephone Expense				GL No: 550	
Date	Description	PR	DR	CR	Balance	
2011						
Apr 22		J1	250		250	DR

Account:	Travel Expense				GL No: 555	
Date	Description	PR	DR	CR	Balance	
2011						
Apr 24		J1	8,000		8,000	DR

AP-7 (❶, ❷, ❸, ❹, ❺, ❻)

High Flying Biplane has completed all their journal entries for the month of June 2011 and posted them to the general ledger. Based on the ledger balances, an unadjusted trial balance has been prepared. Their chart of accounts and unadjusted trial balance are listed below.

Account Description	Account #
ASSETS	
Cash	101
Accounts Receivable	105
Prepaid Insurance	110
Office Supplies	115
Property, Plant & Equipment	120
Accumulated Depreciation	125
LIABILITIES	
Accounts Payable	200
Interest Payable	205
Unearned Revenue	210
Bank Loan	215
OWNER'S EQUITY	
Capital Account	300
Owner's Drawings	310
Income Summary	315

Account Description	Account #
REVENUE	
Service Revenue	400
Interest Earned on Savings	410
EXPENSES	
Advertising Expense	500
Bad Debt Expense	505
Depreciation Expense	510
Insurance Expense	515
Interest Expense	520
Maintenance Expense	525
Office Supplies Expense	530
Professional Fees Expense	535
Rent Expense	540
Salaries Expense	545
Telephone Expense	550
Travel Expense	555

High Flying Biplane
Unadjusted Trial Balance
June 30, 2011

Account Titles	DR	CR
Cash	$8,800	
Accounts Receivable	6,800	
Prepaid Insurance	1,200	
Property, Plant & Equipment	64,000	
Accounts Payable		$7,700
Unearned Revenue		4,700
Bank Loan		19,000
Capital Account		48,800
Owner's Drawings	1,200	
Service Revenue		2,400
Advertising Expense	400	
Telephone Expense	200	
Total	$82,600	$82,600

Note: During the month of June, the owner of High Flying Biplane invested $5,000 into the business.

The following adjustments must be made at the end of June:

Jun 30	One month of prepaid insurance has been used	$100
Jun 30	Depreciation on property, plant and equipment	$450
Jun 30	Unearned revenue that has now been earned	$620
Jun 30	Interest is accrued and owed on the bank loan	$75

Required:

1) Fill in the unadjusted trial balance on the worksheet and complete the rest of the worksheet.
2) Prepare the income statement, statement of owner's equity and the balance sheet.
3) Create the journal entries for the adjustments from the worksheet and post the adjustments to the ledger accounts.
4) Create the closing entries using the income summary account and post the closing entries to the ledger accounts.
5) Prepare the post-closing trial balance.

Note: The daily transactions for the month of June have already been posted in the general ledger. You are only responsible for posting the adjusting and closing entries.

1) Worksheet

High Flying Biplane Worksheet June 30, 2011										
	Unadjusted Trial Balance		Adjustments		Adjusted Trial Balance		Income Statement		Balance Sheet	
Account Titles	Debit	Credit	Debit	Credit	Debit	Credit	Debit	Credit	Debit	Credit

2) Financial Statements

High Flying Biplane Income Statement For the Month Ended June 30, 2011		

High Flying Biplane Statement of Owner's Equity For the Month Ended June 30, 2011		

High Flying Biplane Balance Sheet As at June 30, 2011		

3) Adjusting entries (the general ledger is at the end of this question).

Journal				Page 2
Date	Account Title and Explanation	PR	DR	CR

4) Closing entries (the general ledger is at the end of this question).

Journal				Page 3
Date	Account Title and Explanation	PR	DR	CR

5) Post-closing trial balance.

High Flying Biplane Post-Closing Trial Balance June 30, 2011		
Account Titles	**DR**	**CR**

General Ledger

Account: Cash					GL. No: 101	
Date	**Description**	**PR**	**DR**	**CR**	**Balance**	
2011						
Jun 1	Opening Balance				8,000	DR
Jun 1		J1	5,000		13,000	DR
Jun 2		J1	1,500		14,500	DR
Jun 4		J1		200	14,300	DR
Jun 14		J1		4,000	10,300	DR
Jun 20		J1	1,600		11,900	DR
Jun 22		J1		900	11,000	DR
Jun 24		J1		1,000	10,000	DR
Jun 30		J1		1,200	8,800	DR

Account:	Accounts Receivable				GL No: 105	
Date	**Description**	**PR**	**DR**	**CR**	**Balance**	
2011						
Jun 1	Opening Balance				6,000	DR
Jun 10		J1	2,400		8,400	DR
Jun 20		J1		1,600	6,800	DR

Account:	Prepaid Insurance				GL No: 110	
Date	**Description**	**PR**	**DR**	**CR**	**Balance**	
2011						
Jun 1	Opening Balance				1,200	DR

Account:	Property, Plant & Equipment				GL No: 120	
Date	**Description**	**PR**	**DR**	**CR**	**Balance**	
2011						
Jun 1	Opening Balance				60,000	DR
Jun 14		J1	4,000		64,000	DR

Account:	Accumulated Depreciation				GL No: 125	
Date	**Description**	**PR**	**DR**	**CR**	**Balance**	

Account:	Accounts Payable				GL No: 200	
Date	**Description**	**PR**	**DR**	**CR**	**Balance**	
2011						
Jun 1	Opening Balance				8,200	CR
Jun 3		J1		400	8,600	CR
Jun 22		J1	900		7,700	CR

Account:	Interest Payable				GL No: 205	
Date	**Description**	**PR**	**DR**	**CR**	**Balance**	

Account:	Unearned Revenue				GL No: 210	
Date	**Description**	**PR**	**DR**	**CR**	**Balance**	
2011						
Jun 1	Opening Balance				3,200	CR
Jun 2		J1		1,500	4,700	CR

Account:	Bank Loan				GL No: 215	
Date	Description	PR	DR	CR	Balance	
2011						
Jun 1	Opening Balance				20,000	CR
Jun 24		J1	1,000		19,000	CR

Account:	Capital Account				GL No: 300	
Date	Description	PR	DR	CR	Balance	
2011						
Jun 1	Opening Balance				43,800	CR
Jun 1		J1		5,000	48,800	CR

Account:	Owner's Drawings				GL No: 310	
Date	Description	PR	DR	CR	Balance	
2011						
Jun 30		J1	1,200		1,200	DR

Account:	Income Summary				GL No: 315	
Date	Description	PR	DR	CR	Balance	

Account:	Service Revenue				GL No: 400	
Date	Description	PR	DR	CR	Balance	
2011						
Jun 10		J1		2,400	2,400	CR

Account:	Advertising Expense				GL No: 500	
Date	**Description**	**PR**	**DR**	**CR**	**Balance**	
2011						
Jun 3		J1	400		400	DR

Account:	Depreciation Expense				GL No: 510	
Date	**Description**	**PR**	**DR**	**CR**	**Balance**	

Account:	Insurance Expense				GL No: 515	
Date	**Description**	**PR**	**DR**	**CR**	**Balance**	

Account:	Interest Expense				GL No: 520	
Date	**Description**	**PR**	**DR**	**CR**	**Balance**	

Account:	Telephone Expense				GL No: 550	
Date	**Description**	**PR**	**DR**	**CR**	**Balance**	
2011						
Jun 4		J1	200		200	DR

AP-8 (❶, ❷, ❸, ❹, ❺, ❻)

Limbo Lower has completed all their journal entries for the month of September 2011 and posted them to the general ledger. Based on the ledger balances, an unadjusted trial balance has been prepared. Their chart of accounts and unadjusted trial balance are listed below.

Account Description	Account #
ASSETS	
Cash	101
Accounts Receivable	105
Prepaid Insurance	110
Office Supplies	115
Property, Plant & Equipment	120
Accumulated Depreciation	125
LIABILITIES	
Accounts Payable	200
Interest Payable	205
Unearned Revenue	210
Bank Loan	215
OWNER'S EQUITY	
Capital Account	300
Owner's Drawings	310
Income Summary	315

Account Description	Account #
REVENUE	
Service Revenue	400
Interest Earned on Savings	410
EXPENSES	
Advertising Expense	500
Bad Debt Expense	505
Depreciation Expense	510
Insurance Expense	515
Interest Expense	520
Maintenance Expense	525
Office Supplies Expense	530
Professional Fees Expense	535
Rent Expense	540
Salaries Expense	545
Telephone Expense	550
Travel Expense	555

Limbo Lower
Unadjusted Trial Balance
September 30, 2011

Account Titles	DR	CR
Cash	$5,800	
Accounts Receivable	1,450	
Prepaid Insurance	1,800	
Office Supplies	1,100	
Property, Plant & Equipment	9,300	
Accounts Payable		$3,050
Unearned Revenue		1,400
Bank Loan		4,640
Capital Account		11,450
Owner's Drawings	1,600	
Service Revenue		1,900
Interest Expense	40	
Rent Expense	1,350	
Total	$22,440	$22,440

The following adjustments must be made at the end of September:

Sep 30	One month of prepaid insurance has been used	$150
Sep 30	Depreciation on property, plant and equipment	$120
Sep 30	Unearned revenue that has now been earned	$360
Sep 30	Amount of office supplies used during the month	$450

Required:

1) Fill in the unadjusted trial balance on the worksheet and complete the rest of the worksheet.
2) Prepare the income statement, statement of owner's equity and the balance sheet.
3) Create the journal entries for the adjustments from the worksheet and post the adjustments to the ledger accounts.
4) Create the closing entries using the income summary account and post the closing entries to the ledger accounts.
5) Prepare the post-closing trial balance.

Note: The daily transactions for the month of September have already been posted in the general ledger. You are only responsible for posting the adjusting and closing entries.

1) Worksheet

Limbo Lower Worksheet September 30, 2011												
	Unadjusted Trial Balance		Adjustments		Adjusted Trial Balance		Income Statement		Balance Sheet	
Account Titles	Debit	Credit	Debit	Credit	Debit	Credit	Debit	Credit	Debit	Credit

2) Financial Statements

Limbo Lower Income Statement For the Month Ended September 30, 2011		

Limbo Lower Statement of Owner's Equity For the Month Ended September 30, 2011		

Limbo Lower Balance Sheet As at September 30, 2011		

3) Adjusting entries (the general ledger is at the end of this question).

Journal				Page 2
Date	Account Title and Explanation	PR	DR	CR

4) Closing entries (the general ledger is at the end of this question).

Journal				Page 3
Date	Account Title and Explanation	PR	DR	CR

5) Post-closing trial balance.

Limbo Lower Post-Closing Trial Balance September 30, 2011		
Account Titles	**DR**	**CR**

General Ledger

Account: Cash					GL. No: 101	
Date	**Description**	**PR**	**DR**	**CR**	**Balance**	
2011						
Sep 1	Opening Balance				7,200	DR
Sep 1		J1		1,800	5,400	DR
Sep 2		J1	1,900		7,300	DR
Sep 3		J1		1,350	5,950	DR
Sep 10		J1		40	5,910	DR
Sep 10		J1		960	4,950	DR
Sep 20		J1	2,200		7,150	DR
Sep 22		J1	850		8,000	DR
Sep 24		J1		600	7,400	DR
Sep 30		J1		1,600	5,800	DR

Account: Accounts Receivable					GL No: 105	
Date	**Description**	**PR**	**DR**	**CR**	**Balance**	
2011						
Sep 1	Opening Balance				2,300	DR
Sep 22		J1		850	1,450	DR

Account:	Prepaid Insurance				GL No: 110	
Date	**Description**	**PR**	**DR**	**CR**	**Balance**	
2011						
Sep 1	Opening Balance				0	DR
Sep 1		J1	1,800		1,800	DR

Account:	Office Supplies				GL No: 115	
Date	**Description**	**PR**	**DR**	**CR**	**Balance**	
2011						
Sep 1	Opening Balance				850	DR
Sep 4		J1	250		1,100	DR

Account:	Property, Plant & Equipment				GL No: 120	
Date	**Description**	**PR**	**DR**	**CR**	**Balance**	
2011						
Sep 1	Opening Balance				11,500	DR
Sep 20		J1		2,200	9,300	DR

Account:	Accumulated Depreciation				GL No: 125	
Date	**Description**	**PR**	**DR**	**CR**	**Balance**	

Account:	Accounts Payable				GL No: 200	
Date	**Description**	**PR**	**DR**	**CR**	**Balance**	
2011						
Sep 1	Opening Balance				3,400	CR
Sep 4		J1		250	3,650	CR
Sep 24		J1	600		3,050	CR

Account:	Unearned Revenue				GL No: 210	
Date	**Description**	**PR**	**DR**	**CR**	**Balance**	
2011						
Sep 1	Opening Balance				1,400	CR

Account:	Bank Loan				GL No: 215	
Date	Description	PR	DR	CR	Balance	
2011						
Sep 1	Opening Balance				5,600	CR
Sep 10		J1	960		4,640	CR

Account:	Capital Account				GL No: 300	
Date	Description	PR	DR	CR	Balance	
2011						
Sep 1	Opening Balance				11,450	CR

Account:	Owner's Drawings				GL No: 310	
Date	Description	PR	DR	CR	Balance	
2011						
Sep 30		J1	1,600		1,600	DR

Account:	Income Summary				GL No: 315	
Date	Description	PR	DR	CR	Balance	

Account:	Service Revenue				GL No: 400	
Date	Description	PR	DR	CR	Balance	
2011						
Sep 2		J1		1,900	1,900	CR

Account:	Depreciation Expense				GL No: 510	
Date	Description	PR	DR	CR	Balance	

Account:	Insurance Expense				GL No: 515	
Date	Description	PR	DR	CR	Balance	

Account:	Interest Expense				GL No: 520	
Date	Description	PR	DR	CR	Balance	
2011						
Sep 10		J1	40		40	DR

Account:	Office Supplies Expense				GL No: 530	
Date	Description	PR	DR	CR	Balance	

Account:	Rent Expense				GL No: 540	
Date	Description	PR	DR	CR	Balance	
2011						
Sep 3		J1	1,350		1,350	DR

AP-9 (❺)

Keynote Consulting has journalized their adjusting entries and prepared their adjusted trial balance. Using the adjusted trial balance, prepare the closing entries using the income summary account for the month of August and create the post-closing trial balance.

Keynote Consulting Adjusted Trial Balance August 31, 2011		
Account	**Debit**	**Credit**
Cash	$6,200	
Accounts Receivable	1,750	
Prepaid Insurance	1,650	
Office Supplies	1,150	
Property, Plant and Equipment	10,650	
Accumulated Depreciation		$320
Accounts Payable		1,640
Interest Payable		50
Unearned Revenue		1,420
Bank Loan		3,000
Capital Account		14,290
Owner's Drawings	2,000	
Service Revenue		4,100
Depreciation Expense	150	
Insurance Expense	170	
Interest Expense	50	
Rent Expense	800	
Telephone Expense	250	
Total	$24,820	$24,820

a) Closing entries (ignore the post reference column for this question).

Date	Account Title and Explanation	PR	DR	CR

Date	Account Title and Explanation	PR	DR	CR

b) Post-closing trial balance

Keynote Consulting Post-Closing Trial Balance August 31, 2011		
Account	**Debit**	**Credit**

AP-10 (❺)

Frank's Custom Framing has journalized their adjusting entries and prepared their adjusted trial balance. Using the adjusted trial balance, prepare the closing entries using the income summary account for the month of October and create the post-closing trial balance.

Frank's Custom Framing Adjusted Trial Balance October 31, 2011		
Account	**Debit**	**Credit**
Cash	$8,620	
Accounts Receivable	2,340	
Prepaid Insurance	2,650	
Office Supplies	1,840	
Property, Plant and Equipment	23,400	
Accumulated Depreciation		$1,640
Accounts Payable		3,540
Interest Payable		120
Unearned Revenue		2,110
Bank Loan		5,500
Capital Account		24,080
Owner's Drawings	3,200	
Service Revenue		8,750
Depreciation Expense	260	
Insurance Expense	185	
Interest Expense	120	
Rent Expense	1,200	
Telephone Expense	275	
Salaries Expense	1,650	
Total	$45,740	$45,740

a) Closing entries (ignore the post reference column for this question).

Date	Account Title and Explanation	PR	DR	CR

b) Post-closing trial balance

Frank's Custom Framing Post-Closing Trial Balance October 31, 2011		
Account	**Debit**	**Credit**

AP-11 (❺)

Home Protector has journalized their adjusting entries and prepared their adjusted trial balance. Using the adjusted trial balance, prepare the closing entries directly to the capital account for the month of December and create the post-closing trial balance.

Home Protector Adjusted Trial Balance December 31, 2011		
Account	**Debit**	**Credit**
Cash	$12,650	
Accounts Receivable	5,420	
Prepaid Insurance	2,820	
Office Supplies	2,240	
Property, Plant and Equipment	25,600	
Accumulated Depreciation		$2,340
Accounts Payable		6,250
Salaries Payable		650
Unearned Revenue		4,250
Bank Loan		7,500
Capital Account		21,645
Owner's Drawings	4,300	
Service Revenue		16,875
Depreciation Expense	320	
Insurance Expense	220	
Interest Expense	160	
Rent Expense	1,890	
Telephone Expense	350	
Salaries Expense	3,540	
Total	$59,510	$59,510

a) Closing entries (ignore the post reference column for this question).

Date	Account Title and Explanation	PR	DR	CR

b) Post-closing trial balance

Home Protector Post-Closing Trial Balance December 31, 2011		
Account	**Debit**	**Credit**

AP-12 (❺)

Luminary Electric has journalized their adjusting entries and prepared their adjusted trial balance. Using the adjusted trial balance, prepare the closing entries directly to the capital account for the month of March and create the post-closing trial balance.

Luminary Electric Adjusted Trial Balance March 31, 2011		
Account	**Debit**	**Credit**
Cash	$10,420	
Accounts Receivable	6,350	
Prepaid Insurance	2,350	
Office Supplies	1,860	
Property, Plant and Equipment	32,500	
Accumulated Depreciation		$5,480
Accounts Payable		4,870
Salaries Payable		840
Unearned Revenue		5,340
Bank Loan		9,000
Capital Account		23,745
Owner's Drawings	5,200	
Service Revenue		17,850
Depreciation Expense	410	
Insurance Expense	195	
Interest Expense	210	
Office Supplies Expense	670	
Rent Expense	2,150	
Telephone Expense	450	
Salaries Expense	4,360	
Total	$67,125	$67,125

a) Closing entries (ignore the post reference column for this question).

Date	Account Title and Explanation	PR	DR	CR

b) Post-closing trial balance

Luminary Electric Post-Closing Trial Balance March 31, 2011		
Account	**Debit**	**Credit**

Case Study

CS-1 (❶, ❷, ❸, ❹, ❺)

Grindstone Paving provides residential and commercial paving services. Their balance sheet at the end of June 2011 is shown below, along with their chart of accounts.

Grindstone Paving Balance Sheet As at June 30, 2011			
Assets		**Liabilities**	
Cash	$7,580	Accounts Payable	$15,800
Accounts Receivable	6,000	Unearned Revenue	6,200
Prepaid Insurance	1,800	Bank Loan	22,000
Property, Plant & Equipment	55,000		
		Total Liabilities	44,000
		Owners' Equity	26,380
Total Assets	$70,380	**Total Liabilities & Owners' Equity**	$70,380

Account Description	Account #
ASSETS	
Cash	101
Accounts Receivable	105
Prepaid Insurance	110
Office Supplies	115
Property, Plant & Equipment	120
Accumulated Depreciation	125
LIABILITIES	
Accounts Payable	200
Interest Payable	205
Salary Payable	210
Unearned Revenue	215
Bank Loan	220
OWNER'S EQUITY	
Capital Account	300
Owner's Drawings	310
Income Summary	315

Account Description	Account #
REVENUE	
Service Revenue	400
Interest Earned on Savings	410
EXPENSES	
Advertising Expense	500
Bad Debt Expense	505
Depreciation Expense	510
Insurance Expense	515
Interest Expense	520
Maintenance Expense	525
Office Supplies Expense	530
Professional Fees Expense	535
Rent Expense	540
Salaries Expense	545
Telephone Expense	550
Travel Expense	555

For the month of July 2011, Grindstone Paving had the following transactions:

Jul 1	The owner invested cash into the business	$8,000
Jul 2	Received cash for work that will be provided in August	$2,530
Jul 5	Received an advertising bill which will be paid next month	$600
Jul 8	Paid the telephone bill with cash	$350
Jul 10	Provided services to customers who will pay later	$4,680

Jul 14	Purchase equipment with cash	$8,200
Jul 20	Received payment from customers paying their account	$2,350
Jul 22	Paid part of accounts payable	$1,970
Jul 24	Paid bank loan principal	$1,300
Jul 28	Paid salary to an employee	$2,400
Jul 30	The owner withdrew cash for personal use	$2,200

At the end of July, the following adjustment had to be journalized to properly report the balances of the company's accounts:

Jul 31	One month of prepaid insurance has been used	$100
Jul 31	Depreciation on property, plant and equipment	$450
Jul 31	Unearned revenue that has now been earned	$620
Jul 31	Interest is accrued and owed on the bank loan	$75
Jul 31	Accrued salary expense for an employee	$500

Required:

1) Enter the opening balances from the June 2011 balance sheet into the general ledger accounts (the ledger accounts are presented at the end of this question).
2) Prepare the journal entries for the month of July and post them to the appropriate general ledger accounts.
3) Create the trial balance in the worksheet, and then complete the remaining section of the worksheet.
4) Create the income statement, statement of owner's equity and the balance sheet.
5) Prepare the journal entries for the adjustments and post them to the appropriate general ledger accounts.
6) Prepare the journal entries to close the books for the month of July 2011 (use the income summary account), and post the journal entries to the appropriate general ledger accounts.
7) Create the post-closing trial balance.

Answers:

1) Journal entries

Journal				**Page 1**
Date	**Account Title and Explanation**	**PR**	**DR**	**CR**

Journal				Page 1
Date	**Account Title and Explanation**	**PR**	**DR**	**CR**

2) Worksheet

Grindstone Paving Worksheet July 31, 2011										
	Unadjusted Trial Balance		Adjustments		Adjusted Trial Balance		Income Statement		Balance Sheet	
Account Titles	Debit	Credit	Debit	Credit	Debit	Credit	Debit	Credit	Debit	Credit

3) Financial statements

Grindstone Paving Income Statement For the Month Ended July 31, 2011		

Grindstone Paving Statement of Owner's Equity For the Month Ended July 31, 2011		

Grindstone Paving Balance Sheet As at July 31, 2011		

4) Adjusting entries

Journal				Page 2
Date	**Account Title and Explanation**	**PR**	**DR**	**CR**

5) Closing entries

Journal				Page 3
Date	**Account Title and Explanation**	**PR**	**DR**	**CR**

6) Create the post-closing trial balance.

Grindstone Paving Post-Closing Trial Balance July 31, 2011		
Account Titles	**DR**	**CR**

General Ledger

Account: Cash					**GL. No.**	
Date	**Description**	**PR**	**Debit**	**Credit**	**Balance**	

Account:					**GL. No.**	
Date	**Description**	**PR**	**Debit**	**Credit**	**Balance**	

Account:					**GL. No.**	
Date	**Description**	**PR**	**Debit**	**Credit**	**Balance**	

Account:					**GL. No.**	
Date	**Description**	**PR**	**Debit**	**Credit**	**Balance**	

Account:					**GL. No.**	
Date	**Description**	**PR**	**Debit**	**Credit**	**Balance**	

Account:					**GL. No.**	
Date	**Description**	**PR**	**Debit**	**Credit**	**Balance**	

Account:					**GL. No.**	
Date	**Description**	**PR**	**Debit**	**Credit**	**Balance**	

Account:					GL. No.	
Date	**Description**	**PR**	**Debit**	**Credit**	**Balance**	

Account:					GL. No.	
Date	**Description**	**PR**	**Debit**	**Credit**	**Balance**	

Account:					GL. No.	
Date	**Description**	**PR**	**Debit**	**Credit**	**Balance**	

Account:					GL. No.	
Date	**Description**	**PR**	**Debit**	**Credit**	**Balance**	

Account:					GL. No.	
Date	**Description**	**PR**	**Debit**	**Credit**	**Balance**	

Account:					**GL. No.**	
Date	**Description**	**PR**	**Debit**	**Credit**	**Balance**	

Account:					**GL. No.**	
Date	**Description**	**PR**	**Debit**	**Credit**	**Balance**	

Account:					**GL. No.**	
Date	**Description**	**PR**	**Debit**	**Credit**	**Balance**	

Account:					**GL. No.**	
Date	**Description**	**PR**	**Debit**	**Credit**	**Balance**	

Account:					**GL. No.**	
Date	**Description**	**PR**	**Debit**	**Credit**	**Balance**	

Account:					GL. No.	
Date	Description	PR	Debit	Credit	Balance	

Account:					GL. No.	
Date	Description	PR	Debit	Credit	Balance	

Account:					GL. No.	
Date	Description	PR	Debit	Credit	Balance	

Notes

Chapter 7

MERCHANDISING CORPORATION

Assessment Questions

AS-1 (❶)

What is a merchandising business?

AS-2 (❶)

What do common shares in a corporation represent?

AS-3 (❷)

What does retained earnings in a corporation represent?

AS-4 (❸)

In a perpetual inventory system, how often are inventory levels updated?

AS-5 (❸)

In a periodic inventory system, how often are inventory levels updated?

AS-6 (❹)

Define inventory in the context of a merchandising corporation.

AS-7 (❺)

What does gross profit equal?

AS-8 (❷)

Define operating expenses.

AS-9 (❻)

Define current assets.

AS-10 (❻)

Define non-current assets.

____

____

____

AS-11 (❻)

What are current liabilities? Provide two examples of current liabilities.

____

____

____

AS-12 (❻)

What are non-current liabilities? Provide two examples of non-current liabilities.

____

____

____

AS-13 (❻)

What is one difference between a non-classified balance sheet and a classified balance sheet?

____

____

____

AS-14 (❻)

How do you calculate the current ratio and what does it measure?

____

____

____

AS-15 (❻)

What is one difference between a non-multistep income statement and a multistep income statement?

____

____

____

AS-16 (❻)

What are administrative expenses?

____

____

____

AS-17 (❻)

In a typical multistep income statement, which category will items such as interest revenue and loss from a lawsuit fall under?

____

____

____

Application Questions

AP-1 (❻)

Empowered Inc. has the following balances as at May 31, 2010:

Cash	$22,000
Accounts Receivable	15,000
Inventory	12,000
Property, Plant and Equipment	73,000
Accounts Payable	13,000
Unearned Revenue	8,000
Current Portion of Bank Loan	10,000
Long Term Portion of Bank Loan	20,000
Common Shares	20,000
Retained Earnings	51,000

Required: Prepare a classified balance sheet using the balances listed above.

Empowered Inc. Balance Sheet As At May 31, 2010	

AP-2 (❶, ❷)

The following information is taken from the financial statements of Gray Company during its third year of operations:

	Jan 1, 2011	Dec 31, 2011
Total Assets	$77,000	$89,000
Total Shareholders' Equity	61,000	-
2011 Revenue		22,000
2011 Expenses		15,000
Dividend paid		18,000

Additional information:

Total Shareholders' Equity as at January 1, 2011 is composed of:

Common Shares	$30,000
Retained Earnings	$31,000

Required: Calculate the shareholders' equity on December 31, 2011.

AP-3 (❶, ❷)

Jordan Manufacturing reports the following financial structure for the year ended December 2010:

Current Assets	$105,000
Non-Current Assets	150,000
Current Liabilities	30,000
Non-Current Liabilities	40,000

Calculate shareholders' equity.

AP-4 (❻)

The following information is taken from the records of Ginger Corporation:

Accounts Payable	$19,000
Short-term Investment	12,000
Land	52,000
Cash	23,000
Factory Equipment	29,000
Loans Payable	30,000
Office Furniture	18,000
Prepaid Expense	9,000
Unearned Revenue	6,000

a) Calculate total current assets.

b) Calculate total non-current assets.

c) Calculate total assets.

AP-5 (❻)

Suppose a corporation has $400,000 of long-term bank loan on December 31, 2010. The borrowing arrangement requires the corporation to pay $100,000 of this debt by September 2011. Show how the corporation will report both current and non-current liabilities on its December 31, 2010 balance sheet.

AP-6 (➏)

ABC Corporation borrowed a $1,000,000 interest-free bank loan on January 1, 2010. Payment is agreed to be made in four years in four equal annual installments. Calculate the current and non-current liabilities as at December 31 for the following years.

	December 31			
	2010	**2011**	**2012**	**2013**
Current portion of loan payable				
Non-current loan payable				

AP-7 (➏)

Renegade Corporation's general ledger includes the following account balances on December 31, 2010.

Accounts Payable	$12,000
Interest Payable	3,000
Salaries Payable	2,000
Bank Loan:	
Current Portion	10,000
Long-Term Portion	20,000

a) Calculate current liabilities.

b) Calculate non-current liabilities.

AP-8 (❻)

For the following independent transactions, determine the amount of current and non-current liabilities.

	Transaction	Current	Non-Current
a)	On December 31, 2010, Frankie Co. borrowed $300,000 from the bank. The entire amount is due on December 30, 2011.		
b)	KLM Company purchased a small building at a cost of $190,000. The down payment is $100,000. The remaining balance is payable in 3 years with an annual payment of $30,000, starting next year.		
c)	During June 2010, a business owner obtained an interest-free loan from a financing company. The loan amount was $60,000. The agreed terms of payment is four annual installments of $15,000.		
d)	A business owner borrowed $20,000 from his close friend for a business expansion. They both signed an agreement that the payment will be made after two years.		

AP-9 (❻)

Milward Inc. is a new corporation that was established in April 2011. The corporation had the following transactions for the month of April:

Apr 1	Ray Merck and Jessie Tolley, the owners of the company, invested $50,000 and $70,000 cash into the business, respectively.
Apr 2	Purchased a building that will be used in business operations, for $40,000 cash.
Apr 5	Purchased office furniture worth $7,000, on account.
Apr 10	Borrowed $100,000 bank loan and the amount is to be paid in five years with annual principal payments of $20,000.
Apr 11	Purchased two automobiles worth $30,000 for business use. The amount was fully paid with cash.
Apr 14	Purchased $10,000 of inventory with cash.
Apr 19	Provided $20,000 worth of services to customers; $15,000 cash and $5,000 on credit.
Apr 28	Paid cash for the following expenses during the month:

Advertising	$850
Gas	500
Water	400
Electricity	700
	2,450

Apr 30	Paid $2,000 in salaries for the month

a) Record the journal entries for the above transactions.

Date	Account Title and Explanation	Debit	Credit

b) Prepare a classified balance sheet.

Milward Inc. Balance Sheet As at April 30, 2011	

AP-10 (❻)

The following information is taken from the accounting records of Eternity Corp. for the year ended December 31, 2010.

Current Liabilities:	
Accounts Payable	$20,000
Current portion of bank loan	25,000
Non-Current Liabilities:	
Long-term portion of bank loan	50,000
Shareholders' Equity	80,000

Additional information:

1. Long-term bank loan is payable in annual installments of $25,000 every December 31st.
2. During 2011, the company was able to generate a net income of $15,000 and reduce accounts payable to $7,000.
3. Investors made additional investments of $30,000 cash in 2011.

a) Calculate total liabilities as at December 31, 2011.

b) Calculate shareholders' equity as at December 31, 2011.

AP-11 (❶, ❹)

a) William M. Wilcoxen, an investor, contributed $50,000 to a new business operating as a corporation called W-B Limited. Jerry Bryant, a second investor contributed another $50,000. Prepare the journal entry for W-B Limited to record the new investment.

Date	Account Title and Explanation	Debit	Credit

b) W-B Limited purchased $10,000 worth of inventory with cash. Prepare the journal entry to record the inventory purchase.

Date	Account Title and Explanation	Debit	Credit

c) At the end of the first year of operation, W-B Limited generated sales of $390,000 and their expenses amounted to $380,000 (assume zero taxes). Calculate the following: (1) the net income amount for the first year; and (2) the amount of shareholders' equity at the end of the first year. assume the beginning equity was $100,000.

AP-12 (❶, ❹)

Prepare the journal entry for each of the following transactions for Cosea Limited. These transactions occurred during the month of January 2011.

a) Sylvia Seaberg and Deanna Colin, in return for common shares, contributed $100,000 to a new business operating as a corporation called Cosea Limited.

Date	Account Title and Explanation	Debit	Credit

b) Sylvia and Deanna negotiated a bank loan in the amount of $50,000, payable in equal annual installments over the next five years. Be mindful of the current portion and long-term portion of the loan.

Date	Account Title and Explanation	Debit	Credit

c) The company purchased equipment for $20,000 cash.

Date	Account Title and Explanation	Debit	Credit

d) The company also purchased inventory in the amount of $60,000 with cash.

Date	Account Title and Explanation	Debit	Credit

e) Made sales of $80,000 on account. The cost of the inventory is $60,000.

Date	Account Title and Explanation	Debit	Credit

Date	Account Title and Explanation	Debit	Credit

f) Their insurance company asked the company to pay $1,200 in advance for insurance coverage for one year. The insurance premium is $100 per month. Prepare the journal entry to record the initial prepayment.

Date	Account Title and Explanation	Debit	Credit

During the month, various expenses were incurred. Record the following transactions:

g) Travel expenses were incurred in the amount of $3,000 to be paid next month.

Date	Account Title and Explanation	Debit	Credit

h) Wages were paid with cash in the amount of $18,000.

Date	Account Title and Explanation	Debit	Credit

i) Rent was paid with cash in the amount of $5,000.

Date	Account Title and Explanation	Debit	Credit

At the end of the month, various adjustments were made. Record the following transactions:

j) Recognized $100 of prepaid insurance as an expense.

Date	Account Title and Explanation	Debit	Credit

There were a few more transactions for the month relating to the payment of outstanding debts and the collection of accounts receivable. Record the following transactions:

k) A portion of the outstanding bank loan was paid: $10,000 of principal and $500 of interest.

Date	Account Title and Explanation	Debit	Credit

l) Accounts receivable were collected in the amount of $30,000.

Date	Account Title and Explanation	Debit	Credit

m) Accounts payable were reduced by $3,000.

Date	Account Title and Explanation	Debit	Credit

AP-13 (❻)

Prepare a classified balance sheet using the results of the transactions recorded in AP-12 as at January 31, 2011. Assume that all beginning balances were $0.

Cosea Limited Balance Sheet As at January 31, 2011	

AP-14 (❷)

A company's beginning retained earnings for a period is $2,400. Net income for the period was $3,000. The company did not pay any dividends during this period. Calculate ending retained earnings.

AP-15 (❷)

House Audio Shop is a retailer of high quality audio equipment. It is currently the end of May 2011. The company's retained earnings balance as of May 1, 2011 was $56,000. During May, House Audio Shop earned $10,000 in revenue and incurred $7,500 in expenses. On May 30, 2011, the company declared and paid dividends in the amount of $3,500. What is the balance of retained earnings as at May 31, 2011?

____

____

____

____

AP-16 (❺)

If sales is $300,000 and cost of goods sold is $180,000, what is the gross profit and gross margin percentage?

____

____

____

____

Case Study

CS-1 (❹, ❺, ❻)

George K. Connor operates a company that sells goods and services. During its first month of operations, the following transactions occurred.

Date	Transaction Details	Amount
Feb 1	Received a deposit from a customer for services to be provided later	$6,000
Feb 1	Prepaid insurance for one year with cash	3,600
Feb 3	Sold services for cash	4,000
Feb 5	Sold services to a customer who will pay later	6,000
Feb 7	Recognized unearned revenue as earned	3,000
Feb 11	Paid miscellaneous cash expenses	200
Feb 16	Received an advertising bill which will be paid later	3,000
Feb 20	Purchased inventory - to be paid later	36,000
Feb 21	Sold products on account	31,000
Feb 21	Recorded COGS for products sold	14,000
Feb 22	Paid wages and benefits	6,000
Feb 25	Purchased new computers - to be paid later	4,000
Feb 26	Incurred maintenance expense - to be paid next month	2,000
Feb 27	Customers paid their outstanding account balances owing	3,000
Feb 28	Recognized prepaid insurance for one month	300

The company uses the following chart of accounts to implement its accounting system:

Account Description	Account #
ASSETS	
Cash	101
Accounts Receivable	105
Prepaid Insurance	110
Inventory	115
Property, Plant & Equipment	120
Accumulated Depreciation	125
LIABILITIES	
Accounts Payable	200
Interest Payable	205
Salary Payable	210
Unearned Revenue	215
Bank Loan	220
OWNER'S EQUITY	
Capital Account	300
Owner's Drawings	310
Income Summary	315

Account Description	Account #
REVENUE	
Sales Revenue	400
Sales Returns & Allowances	405
Sales Discount	410
EXPENSES	
Cost of Goods Sold	500
Advertising Expense	505
Depreciation Expense	510
Insurance Expense	515
Maintenance Expense	520
Miscellaneous Expense	525
Office Supplies Expense	530
Professional Fees Expense	535
Rent Expense	540
Salaries Expense	545
Utilities Expense	550
Travel Expense	555

Required:

Prepare the journal entries for the period.
Post the entries to the general ledger.
Prepare a trial balance.
Prepare a multistep income statement for the period.
Prepare a classified balance sheet for the period.
Calculate the gross profit margin on product sales.

Journal **Page 1**

Date	Account Title and Explanation	PR	Debit	Credit

Journal				Page 1
Date	**Account Title and Explanation**	**PR**	**Debit**	**Credit**

ACCOUNT: CASH No.

Date	Description	PR	Debit	Credit	Balance

ACCOUNT: No.

Date	Description	PR	Debit	Credit	Balance

ACCOUNT: No.

Date	Description	PR	Debit	Credit	Balance

ACCOUNT: No.

Date	Description	PR	Debit	Credit	Balance

ACCOUNT: No.

Date	Description	PR	Debit	Credit	Balance

ACCOUNT:					No.
Date	**Description**	**PR**	**Debit**	**Credit**	**Balance**

ACCOUNT:					No.
Date	**Description**	**PR**	**Debit**	**Credit**	**Balance**

ACCOUNT:					No.
Date	**Description**	**PR**	**Debit**	**Credit**	**Balance**

ACCOUNT:					No.
Date	**Description**	**PR**	**Debit**	**Credit**	**Balance**

ACCOUNT:					No.
Date	**Description**	**PR**	**Debit**	**Credit**	**Balance**

ACCOUNT: No.

Date	Description	PR	Debit	Credit	Balance

ACCOUNT: No.

Date	Description	PR	Debit	Credit	Balance

ACCOUNT: No.

Date	Description	PR	Debit	Credit	Balance

ACCOUNT: No.

Date	Description	PR	Debit	Credit	Balance

George K. Connor Worksheet February 28, 2011						
	Trial Balance		Income Statement		Balance Sheet	
Account	**Debit**	**Credit**	**Debit**	**Credit**	**Debit**	**Credit**
Cash						
Accounts Receivable						
Prepaid Insurance						
Inventory						
Property, Plant & Equipment						
Accounts Payable						
Unearned Revenue						
Sales						
Cost of Goods Sold						
Advertising Expense						
Insurance Expense						
Maintenance Expense						
Miscellaneous Expenses						
Salaries Expense						
Totals						
NET INCOME (LOSS)						
TOTAL						

George K. Connor Income Statement For the Month Ended February 28, 2011	

Calculate the gross profit margin on product sales.

George K. Connor Balance Sheet As at February 28, 2011	

Notes

Chapter 8

INVENTORY

Assessment Questions

AS-1 (❶)

Define inventory.

AS-2 (❶)

How often are inventory records updated in a perpetual inventory system?

AS-3 (❶)

How often are inventory records updated in a periodic inventory system?

AS-4 (❷)

What are some reasons purchase returns occur?

AS-5 (❷)

When does a purchase allowance occur?

____

____

____

AS-6 (❷)

Provide three common reasons why a seller gives a discount?

____

____

____

____

AS-7 (❷)

If a discount term is written as 3/10, n/30, what does this mean?

____

____

AS-8 (❷)

What are the two possible Freight on Board (FOB) points?

____

____

AS-9 (❷)

What does FOB shipping point indicate?

____

____

____

AS-10 (❷)

What does FOB destination indicate?

AS-11 (❷)

What type of account is sales returns and allowances and what is it used for?

AS-12 (❷)

What is the formula for gross profit margin?

AS-13 (❸)

List three possible methods used to determine the value of inventory.

AS-14 (❸)

What does FIFO assume?

AS-15 (❸)

Under the weighted average cost method, how do you determine the cost per unit?

AS-16 (❸)

In a period where the cost of purchases increases over time, will FIFO or weighted average method result in the higher value of ending inventory?

AS-17 (❹, ❺)

At what levels of the organization can fraud related to inventory occur? Explain.

Application Questions

AP-1 (❷)

a) Hip Top Shirt Retailers bought $15,000 worth of shirts from Super Shirt Wholesalers Ltd. on March 15th. Payment was due in April. Prepare the journal entry at the time of purchase. Assume they use the perpetual inventory system.

Date	Account Title and Explanation	Debit	Credit

b) Prepare the journal entry for Hip Top Shirt Retailers for the payment of $15,000 made to Super Shirt Wholesalers on April 15th.

Date	Account Title and Explanation	Debit	Credit

AP-2 (❷)

JB Supermarkets bought $3,000 worth of groceries on account from a produce supplier on May 10th. On May 11th, JB's bookkeeper was informed that $200 worth of tomatoes was substandard and returned to the supplier. Prepare the journal entry to record the purchase return. Assume they use the perpetual inventory system.

Date	Account Title and Explanation	Debit	Credit

AP-3 (❷)

On January 12th, Corner-Mart received a shipment of T-shirts from Promo Novelties for an event. The invoice amounted to $5,000 and was recorded in the accounting system. Soon after the delivery was made, the marketing manager discovered that the logo was printed incorrectly. The goods were returned to Promo Novelties on January 31st. Prepare the journal entry that would be recorded on January 31st. Assume Corner-Mart uses the perpetual inventory system.

Date	Account Title and Explanation	Debit	Credit

AP-4 (❷)

a) Signs Unlimited received a shipment of plastic sheets on April 3rd. The value of the plastic was $8,000, plus $100 of freight charges. Prepare the journal entry to record the receipt of goods by Signs Unlimited, assuming the payment for the inventory and freight will be made in May. Assume they use the perpetual inventory system.

Date	Account Title and Explanation	Debit	Credit

b) The plastic sheets delivered to Signs Unlimited were in the wrong colour. After some negotiation, the manager agreed to keep the products with a 10% discount. Prepare the entry on April 10th to record the purchase allowance. (Assume all plastic sheets were still in inventory).

Date	Account Title and Explanation	Debit	Credit

c) Journalize the transaction for Signs Unlimited when the payment is made on May 3rd.

Date	Account Title and Explanation	Debit	Credit

AP-5 (❷)

The following is written on an invoice relating to goods that were purchased: 5/10, n/30. What does it mean?

AP-6 (❷)

a) Shoe Retailers purchased $10,000 worth of shoes from Runner Wear Supplies at the end of March 1st. Since Shoe Retailers has good cash reserves, the accountant took advantage of the early payment discount that Runner Wear offers. Runner Wear's invoice shows terms of 2/10, n/30. What is the latest date that Shoe Retailers could pay the bill to take advantage of the discount?

b) As the bookkeeper for Shoe Retailers, prepare the journal entry to record the purchase on March 1st. Assume they use the perpetual inventory system.

Date	Account Title and Explanation	Debit	Credit

c) Journalize the transaction for payment of the invoice, assuming the payment was made on March 5th.

Date	Account Title and Explanation	Debit	Credit

d) Journalize the transaction for payment of the invoice, assuming the payment was made on March 30th.

Date	Account Title and Explanation	Debit	Credit

AP-7 (❷)

Socks Retailers purchased $10,000 worth of shoes from Jogger Wear Supplies at the end of April 5th. Since Socks Retailers has good cash reserves, the accountant took advantage of the early payment discount that Jogger Wear offers. Jogger Wear's invoice shows terms of 2/15, n/30. What is the latest date that Socks Retailers could pay the bill to take advantage of the discount?

____

____

AP-8 (❷)

At the end of March 20th, Cup-A-Java received a shipment of gift mugs for resale from Cup Makers Inc. in the amount of $5,000, plus $200 shipping charges. The terms stated on the invoice from Cup Makers Inc. were as follows: 3/15, n/60. Assume they use the perpetual inventory system. Journalize the following scenarios:

a) As the bookkeeper for Cup-A-Java, complete the original invoice transaction.

Date	Account Title and Explanation	Debit	Credit

b) If Cup-A-Java decided to take advantage of the early payment cash discount, by when should the payment be made to qualify for the discount?

____

____

c) The payment by Cup-A-Java to Cup Makers Inc. was made on March 31st. Prepare the journal entry for the payment of goods. Discounts only apply to inventory values and not shipping charges.

Date	Account Title and Explanation	Debit	Credit

d) Journalize the entry if payment was made on May 20th.

Date	Account Title and Explanation	Debit	Credit

e) On March 25th, 20% of the shipment was returned because they were in the wrong colour. Cup Makers Inc. agreed to apply the same percentage deduction to the freight charges. The invoice has not been paid. Prepare the journal entry to record this transaction.

Date	Account Title and Explanation	Debit	Credit

f) Continue from (e); journalize the entry if Cup-A-Java took advantage of the early payment cash discount when paying for the balance of the cups on March 31st. Discounts only apply to inventory values and not shipping charges.

Date	Account Title and Explanation	Debit	Credit

AP-9 (❷)

If a computer company bought computers for $10,000 and sold them for $14,000, how much would the gross profit be on the entire shipment if the business took advantage of the early cash payment terms of 2/15, n/30 from their supplier?

____

____

AP-10 (❷)

On May 1st, Food Wholesalers purchased $3,000 worth of dried fruit inventory and paid $100 for freight charges on account. On May 15th, Food Wholesalers sold all of the dried fruit inventory to Retail Grocers for $4,000 on account. As the bookkeeper for Food Wholesalers, journalize the transactions. Assume they use the perpetual inventory system.

Date	Account Title and Explanation	Debit	Credit

AP-11 (❷)

Macks is a maker of cotton garments that are sold to various retailers. On June 1st, Cory's Retailers sent back a shipment of goods that were unsatisfactory. As a gesture of goodwill, Macks agreed to the return of the goods. The goods were sold on account for $6,000 originally and cost $4,000. Assume they use the perpetual inventory system. Complete the following:

a) As Macks' bookkeeper prepare the journal entries to reflect the return.

Date	Account Title and Explanation	Debit	Credit

b) Journalize the entry if Cory's only returned half of the shipment.

Date	Account Title and Explanation	Debit	Credit

c) What happened to the value of Macks' owner's equity when Cory's returned the merchandise? Did it increase, decrease or stay the same? Explain your answer.

____

____

____

____

d) Explain the logic behind debiting the sales returns and allowances as a contra-account instead of debiting the revenue account directly.

____

____

____

____

AP-12 (❷)

Assume you are the bookkeeper for Moira's Wholesalers, a distributor of kitchen furniture. Your sales manager informed you that Ted's Retailers were unhappy with the quality of some tables delivered on August 12th, and they will be shipping back all the goods. The original invoice amounted to $1,500 and the goods cost Moira's $1,000. Assume they use the perpetual inventory system. Complete the journal entries for each of the following scenarios:

a) Rather than taking the tables back, your sales manager agreed to allow Ted's Retailers a 10% discount if they agreed to keep the goods. Record Ted's payment in settlement of the invoice on September 12th.

Date	Account Title and Explanation	Debit	Credit

b) Suppose that Ted's shipped back all the goods on August 15th. Journalize the transactions.

Date	Account Title and Explanation	Debit	Credit

c) Suppose that Ted's shipped back half the goods on August 15th and kept the other half with 10% allowance. Journalize the transactions that took place on August 15th.

Date	Account Title and Explanation	Debit	Credit

d) Continue from part b). Since all the goods were sold and returned in the same period, what happened to Moira's gross profit? (Disregard the additional shipping and administration costs). Explain your answer.

____

____

____

____

AP-13 (❸)

Fill in the missing numbers on the perpetual inventory record. The company uses the weighted average cost for inventory.

Inventory Account					
		Purchase / Sales		Quantity on Hand	
Date	**Description**	**Quantity**	**Amount**	**Quantity**	**Amount**
	Purchase from AAA Co.	200	$2,000	?	?
	Sale to SSS Co.	?	?	100	1,000
	Sale to TTT Co.	-50	?	50	500
	Purchase from BBB	60	720	?	?
	Sale to UUU Co.	-20	?	90	?

Your Answer (fill out):

Inventory Account					
		Purchase / Sales		Quantity on Hand	
Date	**Description**	**Quantity**	**Amount**	**Quantity**	**Amount**

AP-14 (❸)

Use the information from your completed answer to AP - 13. What is the total cost of the units sold to UUU Co. using Specific Identification? Ten of the units sold to UUU were purchased from AAA, and 10 units were purchased from BBB.

AP-15 (❸)

Complete the following table, based on the information completed in AP-13 and AP-14.

	Specific Identification	Average Cost	FIFO
Balance Before Sale to UUU			
COGS on Sale to UUU			
Closing inventory Balance			

AP-16 (❸)

Simplex Inc. has a fiscal year end on December 31. Below is an inventory purchase and sales record for the year 2011. The company has only one product in inventory, and all units of that product are identical (homogenous).

Date	Units Purchased	Units Sold	Units Balance
January 1			15 @ $10 each
February 13	20 @ $12 each		
March 26	15 @ $13 each		
April 17		40 @ $20 each	
July 25	50 @ $14 each		
September 28		35 @ $20 each	
November 3		20 @ $20 each	
December 31			5

Required:

Assume that Simplex Inc. uses the perpetual inventory system and valuates inventory by using the First-In-First-Out (FIFO) method. Calculate the value of cost of goods sold (COGS) for the year.

____

____

____

____

____

AP-17 (❸)

Refer to AP-16 and answer the following:

Assume that Simplex Inc. uses the perpetual inventory system and valuates inventory using the First-In-First-Out (FIFO) method during 2011. Prepare journal entries for recognizing the sale of 35 units at $20 per unit on September 28. Assume that the sale is made on account. For each component of the journal entries, clearly state whether the debit/credit is made to an income statement (I/S) account or a balance sheet (B/S) account. (For example, Dr. Cash (B/S) $10; Cr. Revenue (I/S) $10)

Date	Account Title and Explanation	Debit	Credit

AP-18 (❶)

Suppose that on March 15, both Company A and Company B sold inventory with a cost of $40,000. The updated balance of inventory as at March 1 for both companies was $90,000. Company A uses the perpetual inventory system. Company B uses the periodic inventory system and performs an inventory count at the end of each month. What is the value of inventory on record as at March 15 for each of Company A and Company B.

AP-19 (❹)

Suppose Marcus Apparel Company is experiencing high levels of shrinkage for the past few months of operations. What are two potential red flags that Marcus Apparel Company can observe in order to monitor and prevent inventory shrinkage? Explain.

Case Study

CS-1 (❶, ❷, ❸, ❺)

Rikkers Toys is a retail toy store. They carry several thousand products that are purchased from many different suppliers all over the world. Department managers are responsible for purchasing toys for their respective departments and are measured based on the profitability of their department. While most of their customers pay with cash, there are number of customers that have house accounts and therefore sales are on accounts receivable. Any sales on account have terms of 3/15, net 45.

The department manager for infant toys likes to have her staff rotate stock so the older items are displayed at the front of the shelves and can be sold first. She used to be a manager in a grocery store and has implemented what she learned there. She does not like having extra stock or anything sitting in storage, so she orders just what she thinks she can sell. There have been occasions where some shelves in the infant department have been empty due to lack of stock.

The department manager for toddler toys does not care about rotating stock. In her mind, all products are the same and are not perishable, so rotating stock is irrelevant. This manager likes to ensure that she does not run out of stock, so she always orders enough to keep her shelves stocked. Unfortunately, many times during the year she has too much inventory sitting in storage and has to cut prices to sell the excess stock.

1. Comment on which inventory valuation method would be most appropriate for Rikkers Toys.

2. Examine the way each department manager orders inventory. Are there any problems with how the managers order inventory?

During the month of August, 2011, Rikkers has the following transactions with regards to one of the more popular items they sell, a Crash 'n Go race set. Rikkers currently has 10 race sets in stock at a cost of $10 each. The selling price of the race set is $40.00.

Aug 2	Purchased 15 race sets at $12.00 each. Terms were 2/10, net 30.
Aug 5	Sold eight race sets for cash.
Aug 9	Sold seven race sets to a regular customer on account. Terms were 3/15, net 45.
Aug 10	Purchased 25 race sets at $14.00 each. Terms were 2/10, net 30.
Aug 11	Paid for the purchase from August 2.
Aug 12	Returned five of the race sets purchased on August 10 because they were damaged. Received a credit note from the supplier reducing the amount owing.
Aug 13	Sold six race sets for cash.
Aug 14	The customer from August 9 paid their account in full.
Aug 25	Paid for the purchase from August 10
Aug 31	A physical count of the race sets indicates that there a re 23 race sets in the store. Adjust the inventory, if needed.

3. Assume Rikkers Toys uses FIFO to value their inventory and uses the perpetual inventory system. Record the flow of inventory for the month and then record each transaction in the journal. At the end of the month, prepare an income statement to gross margin.

Fill the table below to demonstrate the inventory levels throughout the month.

Date	Purchases			Sales			Balance		
	Quantity	Unit Cost	Value	Quantity	Unit Cost	Value	Quantity	Unit Cost	Value
Aug 1									
Aug 2									
Aug 5									
Aug 9									
Aug 10									
Aug 12									
Aug 13									
Ending Inventory									

Record the journal entries

Date	Account Title and Explanation	Debit	Credit

Date	Account Title and Explanation	Debit	Credit

What is the amount of gross profit for the month of August?

4. When the cost to purchase a product is increasing, FIFO will provide a higher gross profit and net income than specific identification or weighted average. Suppose Rikkers uses FIFO and the cost to purchase a product is decreasing. If management receives bonuses as a percentage of net income, their bonuses will begin to decrease because FIFO no longer provides the highest gross profit and net income. Can management change their policy and track inventory using a method other than FIFO in order to realize greater bonuses? Explain.

____

____

____

CS-2 (❷)

Freestyle Fashion is a successful urban clothing retailer. Its balance sheet as at January 1, 2011 is presented below.

Freestyle Fashion Balance Sheet As at January 1, 2011		
Current Assets		
Cash	$28,400	
Inventory	50,000	
Prepaid Rent	12,000	
Total Current Assets		$90,400
Non-Current Assets		
Property, Plant & Equipment	32,000	
Total Non-Current Assets		32,000
Total Assets		$122,400
Current Liabilities		
Accounts Payable	$20,500	
Unearned Revenue	12,000	
Total Current Liabilities		$32,500
Non-Current Liabilities		
Bank Loan	60,000	
Total Non-Current Liabilities		60,000
Total Liabilities		92,500
Owner's Equity		29,900
Total Liabilities and Owner's Equity		$122,400

During January, Freestyle Fashion had the following transactions:

Jan 2	Purchased 490 jackets at $50 a piece on account (with terms 2/10, n 30)
Jan 5	Sold $50,000 worth of inventory on account. This inventory cost $39,000
Jan 9	Purchased 100 pairs of jeans at $20 a piece on account (with terms 4/15, n 30)
Jan 11	Paid the balance owed to the supplier for all the jackets purchased on January 2
Jan 16	Paid hourly store workers $2,000 in wages
Jan 18	Products were returned for cash to the store due to a defect. These products were originally sold for $200 and cost $75
Jan 21	Paid the balance owed to the supplier for jeans purchased on Jan 9
Jan 24	Received $25,000 cash from sales previously made on account
Jan 26	Incurred $2,500 in utilities expenses, to be paid next month
Jan 30	Sold $20,000 worth of inventory for cash. This inventory cost $15,000

The company uses the following chart of accounts to implement its accounting system:

Account Description	Account #
ASSETS	
Cash	101
Accounts Receivable	105
Prepaid Rent	110
Inventory	115
Property, Plant & Equipment	120
Accumulated Depreciation	125
LIABILITIES	
Accounts Payable	200
Interest Payable	205
Salary Payable	210
Unearned Revenue	215
Bank Loan	220
OWNER'S EQUITY	
Capital Account	300
Owner's Drawings	310
Income Summary	315

Account Description	Account #
REVENUE	
Sales Revenue	400
Sales Returns & Allowances	405
Sales Discount	410
EXPENSES	
Cost of Goods Sold	500
Advertising Expense	505
Depreciation Expense	510
Insurance Expense	515
Interest Expense	520
Maintenance Expense	525
Office Supplies Expense	530
Professional Fees Expense	535
Rent Expense	540
Salaries Expense	545
Utilities Expense	550
Travel Expense	555

Required:

a) Journalize the transactions for January 2011.

Journal				Page 1
Date	Account Title and Explanation	PR	Debit	Credit

Date	Account Title and Explanation	PR	Debit	Credit

b) Journalize the following adjustments (to be recorded on January 31, 2011):

Jan 31	Prepaid rent represents one year of rent. One month of prepaid rent has been used
Jan 31	Depreciation for the month is $2,000
Jan 31	$1,000 of unearned revenue that has now been earned
Jan 31	$100 of interest is accrued and owed on the bank loan

Journal				Page 2
Date	Account Title and Explanation	PR	Debit	Credit

c) Prepare the month-end closing journal entries. Use the income summary account.

Journal				Page 3
Date	Account Title and Explanation	PR	Debit	Credit

d) Post the transactions to the general ledger.

Note: The Cash, Inventory, Accounts Payable and Sales Revenue accounts have been provided in the ledger.

General Ledger

Account: Cash					GL. No.	
Date	Description	PR	Debit	Credit	Balance	

Account:					GL. No.	
Date	Description	PR	Debit	Credit	Balance	

Account:					GL. No.	
Date	Description	PR	Debit	Credit	Balance	

Account: Inventory					GL. No.	
Date	Description	PR	Debit	Credit	Balance	

Account:					GL. No.	
Date	Description	PR	Debit	Credit	Balance	

Account:					GL. No.	
Date	Description	PR	Debit	Credit	Balance	

Account: Accounts Payable					GL. No.	
Date	Description	PR	Debit	Credit	Balance	

Account:					GL. No.	
Date	Description	PR	Debit	Credit	Balance	

Account:					GL. No.	
Date	Description	PR	Debit	Credit	Balance	

Account:					GL. No.	
Date	Description	PR	Debit	Credit	Balance	

Account:					GL. No.	
Date	Description	PR	Debit	Credit	Balance	

Account:					GL. No.	
Date	**Description**	**PR**	**Debit**	**Credit**	**Balance**	

Account: Sales Revenue					GL. No.	
Date	**Description**	**PR**	**Debit**	**Credit**	**Balance**	

Account:					GL. No.	
Date	**Description**	**PR**	**Debit**	**Credit**	**Balance**	

Account:					GL. No.	
Date	**Description**	**PR**	**Debit**	**Credit**	**Balance**	

Account:					GL. No.	
Date	**Description**	**PR**	**Debit**	**Credit**	**Balance**	

Account:					**GL. No.**	
Date	**Description**	**PR**	**Debit**	**Credit**	**Balance**	

Account:					**GL. No.**	
Date	**Description**	**PR**	**Debit**	**Credit**	**Balance**	

Account:					**GL. No.**	
Date	**Description**	**PR**	**Debit**	**Credit**	**Balance**	

Account:					**GL. No.**	
Date	**Description**	**PR**	**Debit**	**Credit**	**Balance**	

e) Prepare a multistep income statement, statement of owner's equity, and a classified balance sheet for January 2011.

Freestyle Fashion **Income Statement** **For the Month Ended January 31, 2011**		

Freestyle Fashion **Statement of Owner's Equity** **For the Month Ended January 31, 2011**		

Freestyle Fashion **Balance Sheet** **As at January 31, 2011**		

Chapter 9

CASH CONTROLS

Assessment Questions

AS-1 (➊)

What is a bank reconciliation?

AS-2 (➊)

List three typical reasons for the bank making additional deductions from the company's cash account?

AS-3 (➊)

What are two typical reasons for the bank making additional deposits to the company's cash account?

AS-4 (➊)

In a typical bank reconciliation, what are the titles of the two column headers?

AS-5 (❶)

What are non-sufficient funds (NSF) cheques?

AS-6 (❶)

What is an outstanding deposit?

AS-7 (❶)

When is a journal entry required during a bank reconciliation?

AS-8 (❶)

How are outstanding cheques recorded on the bank reconciliation?

AS-9 (❷)

What is an imprest system (in the context of petty cash)?

AS-10 (❷)

Briefly describe the responsibilities of the petty cash custodian.

AS-11 (❷)

What does an employee that requires petty cash need to present to the petty cash custodian?

AS-12 (❷)

What is a petty cash summary sheet?

AS-13 (❷)

Why do petty cash overages or shortages occur?

AS-14 (❷)

When does the cash over and short account behave like an expense account?

AS-15 (❷)

What are the only two times that the petty cash account in the ledger is debited or credited?

___

___

___

AS-16 (❸)

List two general controls that can be used for petty cash.

___

___

___

AS-17 (❸)

List two controls that can be used to prevent the misuse of cash?

___

___

___

Application Questions

AP-1 (❶)

Quality Electronic Corporation is preparing a bank reconciliation and has identified the following potential reconciling items. For each item, indicate if it is (i) added to the balance of the ledger, (ii) deducted from the balance of the ledger, (iii) added to the balance of the bank statement, or (iv) deducted from the balance of the bank statement.

a) Deposits that are not shown on the bank statement
b) Interest deposited to the company's account
c) Bank service charges
d) Outstanding cheques
e) NSF cheques returned

AP-2 (❶)

The following data represents information necessary to assist in preparing the June 30th bank reconciliation for Trimore Company Inc.

a) The June 30th bank balance was $5,300
b) The bank statement indicated a deduction of $30 for bank service charges
c) A customer deposited $1,200 directly into the bank account to settle an outstanding accounts receivable bill
d) Cheque number 850 for $600 and cheque number 857 for $420 have been recorded in the company ledger but did not appear on the bank statement
e) A customer paid an amount of $4,534 to Trimore on the 30th of June but the deposit did not appear on the bank statement
f) The accounting clerk made an error and recorded a $200 cheque as $2,000. The cheque was written to pay outstanding accounts payable account

g) Cheque number 9574 for $100 was deducted from Trimore's account by the bank. This cheque was not written by Trimore and needs to be reversed by the bank.

h) The bank included an NSF cheque in the amount of $820 relating to a customer's payment.

i) The general ledger cash account showed a balance of $6,764 on June 30th

Required:

1. Complete the bank reconciliation for Trimore Company
2. Write the necessary journal entries to correct Trimore's records

		Bank	Ledger

Date	Account Title and Explanation	Debit	Credit

Date	Account Title and Explanation	Debit	Credit

Date	Account Title and Explanation	Debit	Credit

Date	Account Title and Explanation	Debit	Credit

AP-3 (❶)

a) Prepare the July 2010 bank reconciliation statement for World's Computer Inc. using the following information

- Cash balance per general ledger is $2,219
- Bank statement balance is $2,478.80
- These cheques were recorded in the ledger but did not appear on the bank statement. They are: Cheque #186 for $100; Cheque #193 for $57; Cheque #199 for $143.
- A deposit for $368 dated July 31 was recorded in the ledger but did not appear on the bank statement
- Service charges of $18 are shown on the bank statement
- A cheque for $37.50 has been cashed (correctly) by the bank but was incorrectly recorded in the company's ledger as $375.50. The cheque was issued for the purchase of office supplies.
- The bank automatically deposited interest of $7.80 at the end of the month.

b) In a general journal, record any entries required to bring the company records up to date.

Your Answers:

a)

World's Computer Inc. Bank Reconciliation Statement July 31, 2010		
Explanation	**Ledger**	**Bank**

b)

Date	Account Title and Explanation	Debit	Credit

AP-4 (❶)

Mike's Cleaning Service received its monthly bank statement for its business bank account, with a balance of $55,062 for the month of July 2011. The total for the ledger account as at July 31, 2011 was $59,461. After a comparison of the cheques written by the company and those deducted from the bank account, Mike's accountant determined that three cheques, totaling $2,806 (No. 256 - $606, No. 261 - $1,200, No. 262 - $1,000), were outstanding on July 31. A review of the deposits showed that a deposit on July 1 for $12,610 was actually recorded in the company's ledger on June 30 and a July 31 deposit of $9,760 was recorded in the company's ledger on the date but had not been recorded by the bank yet. The July bank statement showed a service fee of $18, a customer's cheque in the amount of $70 that had been returned NSF, a loan payment of $857 that was deducted automatically by the bank, and a customer automatically made a $3,500 payment which was deposited into Mike's Cleaning bank account.

Required:

a) Prepare bank reconciliation as at July 31.

b) How much cash does Mike's Cleaning Service actually have in its cash account on July 31?

c) Prepare adjusting journal entries to record all necessary adjustments to bring the cash account to its adjusted balance.

a)

Mike's Cleaning Service Bank Reconciliation Statement July 31, 2011		
Explanation	**Ledger**	**Bank**

b) ____________________

c)

Date	Account Title and Explanation	Debit	Credit

AP-5 (❶)

The following T-Account contains information about RJ Cosmetics' cash account:

Cash			
Opening Balance Feb 1	4,000	Feb 3	800
Feb 12	2,500	Feb 21	1,200
Feb 28	1,000	Feb 26	950
		Feb 27	600
	3,950		

This is RJ Cosmetics' bank statement for the month of February.

Date	Explanation	Withdrawal	Deposit	Balance
Feb 01	Opening Balance			4,000
Feb 03	Cheque # 1	800		3,200
Feb 12	Deposit		2,500	5,700
Feb 14	NSF Cheque	500		5,200
Feb 14	NSF Charge	15		5,185
Feb 21	Cheque # 2	1,200		3,985
Feb 25	EFT - Monthly Rent expense	1,000		2,985
Feb 28	Service Charges	25		2,960
Feb 28	Interest on Bank Account		20	2,980
		3,540	2,520	

a) Prepare a bank reconciliation for RJ Cosmetics.

RJ Cosmetics Bank Reconciliation February 28, 2010		
	Ledger	**Bank**

b) Prepare the required journal entries for the corrections made in the bank reconciliation.

Date	Account Title and Explanation	Debit	Credit

c) Prepare a corrected cash T-Account.

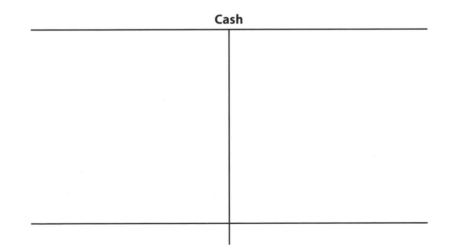

Cash	

AP-6 (❶)

Shine Laundry's bank reconciliation is provided for the month of September. However, due to some errors on the bank reconciliation, the corrected balance for the ledger and the bank are different from each other.

Shine Laundry Bank Reconciliation September 30, 2010		
	Ledger	**Bank**
Balance as per records	5,100	3,820
Add: Outstanding deposit - Sep 29	400	
Outstanding deposit - Sep 30	1,220	
Less: Outstanding cheque # 3 - Sep 8		(1,000)
Outstanding cheque # 4 - Sep 10	(600)	
EFT - Insurance - Sep 15		(400)
EFT - Monthly rent - Sep 18		(600)
NSF cheque - Sep 19		(250)
Charges for NSF cheque - Sep 19		(5)
Service charges - Sep 30	(15)	
Interest on bank account - Sep 30	(10)	
Corrected Balance	6,095	1,565

Required:

a) Prepare a corrected bank reconciliation. Assume the dollar amounts of the individual items on the bank reconciliation are correct.

Shine Laundry Bank Reconciliation September 30, 2010		
	Ledger	**Bank**

b) Prepare all journal entries that would be required by Shine Laundry.

Date	Account Title and Explanation	Debit	Credit

AP-7 (❶)

For the month of September 2010, Jared Anitco has noticed that the bank has processed a cheque that he was not aware of. As a result, he calls the bank and determines that the cheque belongs to another account. The following is the general ledger report for cash in the bank and bank statement for Jared Anitco for the month of September.

GENERAL LEDGER - BANK				
Date	**Explanation**	**Debit**	**Credit**	**Balance**
Sep 1	Opening Balance			7,000
Sep 6	CandyMan Cheque # 200		500	6,500
Sep 6	Supply Store - Cheque # 201		754	5,746
Sep 10	Jordan Lo - Cheque #1000	800		6,546
Sep 25	Book Store - Cheque #202		200	6,346

BANK STATEMENT				
Date	**Explanation**	**Withdrawal**	**Deposit**	**Balance**
Sep 1	Opening Balance			7,000
Sep 10	CandyMan Cheque # 200	500		6,500
Sep 10	Supply Store - Cheque # 201	754		5,746
Sep 14	Jordan Lo - Cheque #1000		800	6,546
Sep 20	Mooris Mo - Cheque#1107	820		5,726
Sep 30	Book Store - Cheque #202	200		5,526

Required:

Identify the cheque that does not belong to Jared. If necessary, prepare the required journal entries.

Date	Account Title and Explanation	Debit	Credit

AP-8 (❶)

Consider the following general ledger and bank statement for Meena Salon.

GENERAL LEDGER - BANK				
Date	**Explanation**	**Debit**	**Credit**	**Balance**
Apr 1	Opening Balance			8,000
Apr 6	Jimmy Supplies - Cheque # 101		500	7,500
Apr 10	HitHit Supplies - Cheque # 102		1,000	6,500
Apr 11	Mary Malony	250		6,750
Apr 14	Inner Beauty Inc. - Cheque # 103		757	5,993
Apr 19	Shona Care Ltd. - Cheque # 104		840	5,153
Apr 29	Deposit	2,500		7,653

BANK STATEMENT				
Date	**Explanation**	**Withdrawal**	**Deposit**	**Balance**
Apr 1	Opening Balance			8,000
Apr 6	Cheque # 101	500		7,500
Apr 10	Cheque # 102	1,000		6,500
Apr 10	EFT - Monthly Rent	800		5,700
Apr 11	Mary Malony		250	5,950
Apr 11	NSF Cheque	250		5,700
Apr 11	NSF Charge	5		5,695
Apr 14	Cheque # 103	575		5,120
Apr 21	Cheque # 1520	3,000		2,120
Apr 30	Service Charges	25		2,095
Apr 30	Interest on Bank Account		20	2,115
		6,155	270	

Additional Information:

1. On April 14, Meena Salon purchased $575 worth of salon supplies from Inner Beauty Inc.
2. The salon's cheque numbers are always three-digits in length.

Required:

a) Prepare a bank reconciliation for Meena Salon on April 30, 2011.

Meena Salon Bank Reconciliation April 30, 2011		
Explanation	**Ledger**	**Bank**

b) Prepare the necessary journal entries.

Date	Account Title and Explanation	Debit	Credit

AP-9 (❶)

The bank statement for Fashion Fly Inc. had an ending cash balance of $1,500 on December 31, 2010. On this date the cash balance in their general ledger was $2,000. After comparing the bank statement with the company records, the following information was determined:

- The bank returned an NSF cheque in the amount of $320 that Fashion Fly Inc. deposited on December 20th.
- Direct deposit received from a customer on December 30th in payment of their accounts totaling $3,850. This has not yet been recorded by the company.
- On December 30th the bank deposited $10 for interest earned.
- The bank withdrew $20 for bank service charges
- Deposits in transit on December 31st totaled $4,020

Required: Reconcile the ledger and bank statement and create the required journal entries.

Fashion Fly Inc. Bank Reconciliation December 31, 2010		
Explanation	**Ledger**	**Bank**

Date	Account Title and Explanation	Debit	Credit

AP-10 (❷)

On June 7, Mary decided to use a petty cash fund for her small business. A cheque of $125 was issued and cashed. The $125 cash was given to the store supervisor who was to act as petty cashier. The petty cashier was told to obtain authorized vouchers for all payments. Petty cash was to be replenished when the balance in the cash box reached $23.

a) Record the establishment of the fund on June 7.

b) On June 19, this summary was prepared:

Delivery Expense	$50.90
Miscellaneous Expense	20.40
Office Expense	24.10
Postage Expense	6.60
Total	102

Prepare the entry to replenish the petty cash.

c) On June 23, it was decided to increase the amount of the petty cash fund from $125 to $175. A cheque of $50 was issued. Record the transaction.

a)

Date	Account Title and Explanation	Debit	Credit

b)

Date	Account Title and Explanation	Debit	Credit

c)

Date	Account Title and Explanation	Debit	Credit

AP-11 (❷)

The petty cash fund was established on August 12, 2010 in the amount of $250.00. Expenditures from the fund by the custodian as of August 31, 2010, were evidenced by approved receipts for the following:

Postage expense	$30.00
Supplies expense	65.00
Maintenance expense	42.00
Shipping charges	58.20
Newspaper advertising	21.95
Miscellaneous expense	15.75

On August 31, 2010, the petty cash fund was replenished and increased to $300.00; currency and coin in the fund at that time totaled $15.60.

Required:

Prepare the journal entries to record the transactions related to the petty cash fund for the month of August.

Date	Account Title and Explanation	Debit	Credit

Date	Account Title and Explanation	Debit	Credit

AP-12 (❷, ❸)

Last year, Holtzman Company established a petty cash fund of $100. The custodian complained that she had to reimburse the fund on a weekly basis, and suggested that the fund be increased to $400. That way, she would only have to summarize payouts and get a cheque from the cashier once per month.

Management agreed with the custodian, and on April 1 advised the cashier to increase the fund to $400.

a) Write the journal entry to increase the fund to $400.

b) List at least five internal controls that should be established around the use of petty cash.

a)

Date	Account Title and Explanation	Debit	Credit

b)

AP-13 (❷)

On March 20th, Skyline Enterprises established a $300 petty cash fund.

a) Prepare the entry to record the establishment of the fund.

b) At the end of the month, the petty cash custodian analyzed all the monthly transactions. She opened the petty cash box and counted $100 cash remaining. There were also two receipts in the petty cash box: receipt # 1: $100 – Entertainment and receipt #2: $98 – Travel. Record the journal entries for this month's expenses and replenish the fund.

c) At the end of the month, Skyline Enterprises wanted to increase the petty cash fund by $100. Prepare the journal entry to record the increase in petty cash fund.

a)

Date	Account Title and Explanation	Debit	Credit

b)

Date	Account Title and Explanation	Debit	Credit

c)

Date	Account Title and Explanation	Debit	Credit

AP-14 (❷)

On January 1, 2010, Hit Design Inc. set up a petty cash fund for $250.
At the end of the first week, the petty cash fund contains the following:

Cash on hand	$50
Receipt for the purchase of office supplies	40
Receipt for shipping charges	10
Receipt for the purchase of stamps	20
Receipt for travel to a client meeting	50
Receipt for the payment of newspaper advertising	75

Required:

a) Calculate any cash overage or shortage.

b) Prepare the journal entries for setting up and replenishing the petty cash fund.

Date	Account Title and Explanation	Debit	Credit

AP-15 (❷)

The following information was taken from the records of the JoJo Store.

Apr 14	Paid $25 for public transit
Apr 16	Paid $20 for food
Apr 17	Purchased stamps for $5
Apr 17	Paid $50 for window washing
Apr 19	Paid $15 for the delivery of packages
Apr 20	Purchased office supplies for $30

JoJo is the owner of the store and he established a petty cash fund of $200 on April 12, 2010. All the transactions listed above were paid using petty cash. Petty cash needs to be replenished when $50 is left in the petty cash box. On April 21, there was $50 left in the petty cash box.

Required: Prepare the journal entries for setting up and replenishing the petty cash fund.

Date	Account Title and Explanation	Debit	Credit

AP-16 (❷)

On April 1, 2011, Clayton Company established a petty cash fund of $200.

During the month the custodian paid out the following amounts:

April 6	Purchased stamps	$40
April 8	Freight on incoming package	20
April 10	Public transit fares for employees on company business	25
April 14	Coffee and donuts for clients during a meeting	8
April 15	Package of paper for the copy machine	7

The custodian counted the fund on April 16th and found $105 in the petty cash box.

Required:

a) Prepare the journal entry to record the establishment of the fund.

Date	Account Title and Explanation	Debit	Credit

b) Prepare the journal entry to record the reimbursement of the fund on April 16, 2011.

Date	Account Title and Explanation	Debit	Credit

Case Study

CS-1 (❸)

M & G Block (M & G) is an incorporated tax preparation company. Most of its clients pay for the completion of their tax returns with either a debit or a credit card. The rest pay with actual cash.

At the office in Toronto, Ontario, M & G has employed 20 tax preparers, two supervisors and a manager. The office collects thousands of dollars in cash every day. After a tax return is prepared by one of the 20 tax preparers, a supervisor is responsible for recording information (i.e. customer name, amount charged, payment method) related to the return in a log.

The receipt of cash is recorded immediately when it is received. Receipts are issued immediately, in numerical order. Copies of the receipts are also kept with the logs. The cash is kept in the drawer of the employee who prepared the tax return. At the end of the day, the cash being kept by the various employees are pooled together and then passed on to the supervisor, who will keep it in his drawer. The cash is deposited into the bank at the end of each work week.

Over the past few weeks, the manager has noted that the amount of cash on hand in the office has consistently been less than the amount recorded in the logs. In fact, the difference between the actual cash on hand and the recorded amount is increasing little by little over time.

Required:

a) Is M & G exhibiting any positive aspects in its system of cash controls? Explain.

b) What are the negatives in M & G's cash control system? Explain. (You can refer to controls that do not exist, or controls that exist but are ineffective).

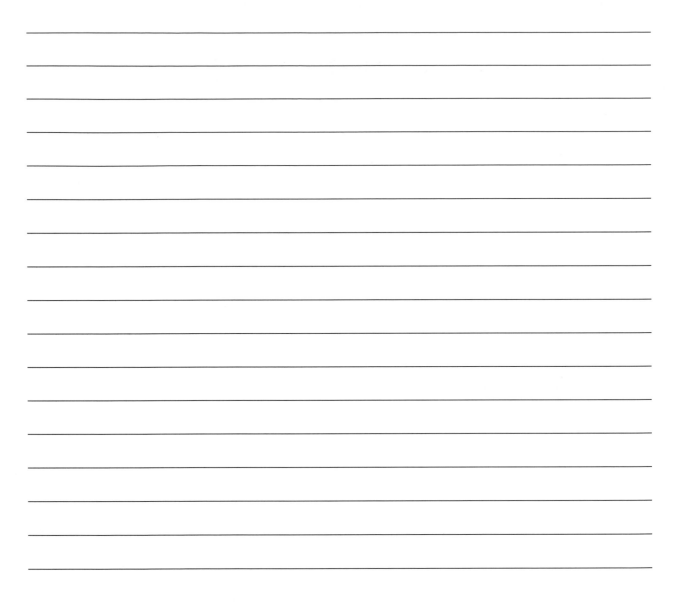

Chapter 10

PAYROLL

Assessment Questions

AS-1 (❶)

Define gross pay.

____

____

AS-2 (❶)

What is net pay?

____

____

AS-3 (❶)

Identify two differences between employees who are paid a salary and employees who are paid hourly.

____

____

____

AS-4 (❶)

Define statutory deductions, and identify the three statutory deductions in Canada.

____

____

____

AS-5 (➊)

Define voluntary deductions, and provide three examples of voluntary deductions.

AS-6 (➊)

What is the purpose of workers' compensation?

AS-7 (➋)

True or False: There is no maximum amount for the Canada Pension Plan (CPP) deductions, so employees will contribute to the CPP no matter how much they earn in a year.

AS-8 (➋)

How much is the annual CPP exemption amount, and what does it mean for employees?

AS-9 (➌)

How much must the employer contribute to CPP on behalf of their employees?

AS-10 (❷)

Is there any limitation to the amount of Employment Insurance (EI) that will be deducted from an employee's pay (i.e. age, exemption amounts or maximum deductions)?

AS-11 (❸)

How much must the employer contribute to EI on behalf of their employees?

AS-12 (❷)

Is there any limitation to the amount of income tax that will be deducted from an employee's pay (i.e. age, exemption amounts or maximum amounts)?

AS-13 (❹)

True or False: The total cost of paying an employee is equal to the amount of gross pay the employee earns.

AS-14 (❺)

What type of information would be recorded in a payroll record and what is the information used for?

AS-15 (❺)

When would a company use a payroll register?

AS-16 (❻)

Identify two payroll controls and briefly explain them.

AS-17 (❻)

How does an imprest bank account help control payroll?

Application Questions

AP-1 (➊)

1. Identify the following payroll deductions and expenses as statutory or voluntary, based on legislation.

Description	Statutory	Voluntary
Income Taxes		
Dental benefits		
Union dues		
Savings bond purchase		
Uniform allowance		
Tuition		
Canada Pension Plan		
Prescription coverage		
Retirement deduction		
Employment Insurance		
Long-term disability		
Professional dues		
Charitable donations		
Tools and safety apparel		

AP-2 (➊)

ABC Company showed the following information relating to employees' salaries for the month:

Gross wages	$4,300
Taxes withheld	600
Canada Pension Plan contributions	120
Employment Insurance contributions	250

Note: The company matches 100% of employees' pension and 140% of employees' employment insurance.

Required:

a) Calculate the company's total expense.

b) Calculate the employee's net pay.

AP-3 (❶)

The records of Dipsum Soft Drinks show the following figures:

Employee Earnings	
Salaries for the month	?
Overtime Pay	2,200
Total	?
Deductions and Net Pay	
Withheld Statutory Deductions	990
Charitable Contributions	?
Medical Insurance	780
Total Deductions	2,270
Net Pay	6,630

Required:

Calculate the missing amounts.

AP-4 (❶)

Hurley Johnson works as a janitor in a hospital and earns a wage rate of $8.00 per hour. Johnson's payroll deductions include withheld income tax of 7% of total earnings, pension of $200, employment insurance amounting to $330, and a monthly deduction of $40 for a charitable contribution.

Required:

Calculate Hurley Johnson's gross pay and net pay assuming he worked 168 hours during the month.

AP-5 (❶, ❷, ❸)

An employer has calculated the following amounts for an employee during the last week of January:

Gross wages	$1,500
Taxes withheld	325
Canada Pension Plan contributions	110
Employment Insurance contributions	35

a) Calculate the employee's net pay:

b) Assuming the employer's contribution is 100% for Pension Plan and 140% for Employment Insurance, what is the employer's total expense?

c) Prepare the journal entries to record payroll for the employee and record the employer's contribution:

Date	Account Title and Explanation	Debit	Credit

AP-6 (❶, ❷, ❸)

An employer has calculated the following amounts for an employee during the last week of February:

Gross wages	$1,800
Taxes withheld	375
Canada Pension Plan contributions	125
Employment Insurance contributions	45
Worker's Compensation	20

a) Calculate the employee's net pay:

b) Assuming the employer's contribution is 100% for Pension Plan and 140% for Employment Insurance, what is the employer's total expense?

c) Prepare the journal entries to record payroll for the employee and record the employer's contribution:

Date	Account Title and Explanation	Debit	Credit

AP-7 (❶, ❷, ❸, ❺)

The payroll records of Russon Corporation's district office provided the following information for the weekly pay period ended December 31, 2011.

Employee	Hours worked	Hourly Rate	Income Tax	Pension Plan	Employment Insurance	Dues
Clay York	43 hrs	$12	$78	$14	$13	$10
Karen Cooper	46 hrs	15	89	15	14	10
Stephen James	48 hrs	17	102	18	12	10
Jessie Moore	40 hrs	14	90	13	10	10

Note:
All employees are paid 1.5 times their hourly wage for hours worked in excess of 40 hours per week. The company contributes 100% for its share of pension plan and 140% of employment insurance.

Required:

a) Calculate gross and net pay for each employee. Round all answers to the nearest whole number.

Employee	Gross Pay	Income Tax	Pension Plan	Employment Insurance	Dues	Net	Employer's Cost: Pension Expense	Employer's Cost: Employment Insurance
Clay York								
Karen Cooper								
Stephen James								
Jessie Moore								
Total								

b) Prepare the payroll journal entries for December 31, 2011.

Date	Account Title and Explanation	Debit	Credit

c) Prepare a journal entry to record cash payment of all liabilities on January 2, 2012.

Date	Account Title and Explanation	Debit	Credit

AP-8 (❶, ❷, ❸, ❹, ❺)

Learn Company has four employees who are paid on an hourly basis, plus time and one half for hours in excess of 40 hours per week. Payroll information for the week ending June 15th is listed below:

Employee	Total Hours	Hourly Rate	Income Tax	CPP	EI	Union Dues
A. Bee	40	$9.50	$57.00	$15.48	$6.76	$25.00
E. Fields	47	11.00	83.33	24.17	9.89	0.00
L. Parsons	42	11.75	75.79	21.68	8.99	15.00
I. Jay	44	10.50	72.45	20.58	8.60	15.00

a) Assume the employer contributes 100% towards the pension plan and 140% towards employment insurance. Calculate gross and net pay for each employee:

Payroll Register							
		Deductions					
Employee	Gross*	Income Tax	CPP	EI	Union Dues	Total Deductions	Net Pay
A. Bee							
E. Fields							
L. Parsons							
I. Jay							
Total							

*Remember to calculate time and one half for overtime hours.

b) Prepare the payroll journal entries for June 15th to pay the employees and accrue the employer contributions:

Date	Account Title and Explanation	Debit	Credit

c) Prepare the journal entry to record the cash payment on June 30th for the employer's liability to the government:

Date	Account Title and Explanation	Debit	Credit

AP-9 (❶, ❷, ❸, ❹, ❺)

Tremolo Manufacturing has three employees who work on an hourly basis and are paid bi-weekly. The current CPP rate is 4.95%, the current EI rate is 1.78%, and the appropriate income tax rate is 18%. Each employee contributes a portion of their pay to the United Way. The employer pays the entire amount of the health care premium for the employees. Assume the employer contributes 100% towards the pension plan and 140% towards employment insurance. Payroll information for the week ending August 20, 2011 is listed below:

Employee	Total Hours	Hourly Rate	United Way	Health Care
Sing Ing	80	$12.50	$5.00	$14.00
Roc N. Role	78	14.00	7.00	20.00
Hip Hopp	75	13.50	4.00	17.00

a) Calculate gross and net pay for each employee:

Payroll Register							
		Deductions					
Employee	**Gross**	**Income Tax**	**CPP***	**EI**	**United Way**	**Total Deductions**	**Net Pay**
Sing Ing							
Roc N. Role							
Hip Hopp							
Total							

*Remember to properly account for the $3,500 exemption

b) Calculate the employer contributions:

Employer Contributions	
CPP	
EI	
Health Care	

c) Prepare the payroll journal entries for August 20, 2011 to record the salaries payable to the employees and accrue the employer contributions:

Date	Account Title and Explanation	Debit	Credit

d) Prepare the entry to pay the employees on August 23, 2011:

Date	Account Title and Explanation	Debit	Credit

e) Prepare the entries to pay the liabilities to the United Way and the health insurance company on August 31, 2011:

Date	Account Title and Explanation	Debit	Credit

f) Prepare the entry to pay the liabilities to the government on September 15, 2011:

Date	Account Title and Explanation	Debit	Credit

AP-10 (❶, ❷, ❸, ❹, ❺)

Rippling Waters rents canoes and other water crafts to campers and hikers. On May 15, 2011, Rippling Waters prepared their semi-monthly payroll for their employees. The current CPP rate is 4.95%, the current EI rate is 1.78%, and the appropriate income tax rate is 20%. The employer pays half of the health care premium, and the employees pay the other half. Assume the employer contributes 100% towards the pension plan and 140% towards employment insurance. Payroll information for May 15, 2011 is listed below:

Employee	Total Hours	Hourly Rate	Health Care
M. Swift	87.5	$14.50	$18.00
S. Current	85.5	15.00	20.00
B. Wavey	73.5	13.50	14.00

a) Calculate gross and net pay for each employee:

Payroll Register							
		Deductions					
Employee	**Gross**	**Income Tax**	**CPP***	**EI**	**Health Care**	**Total Deductions**	**Net Pay**
M. Swift							
S. Current							
B. Wavey							
Total							

*Remember to properly account for the $3,500 exemption

b) Calculate the employer contributions:

Employer Contributions	
CPP	
EI	
Health Care	

c) Prepare the payroll journal entries for May 15, 2011 to record the salaries payable to the employees and accrue the employer contributions:

Date	Account Title and Explanation	Debit	Credit

d) Prepare the entry to pay the employees on May 17, 2011:

Date	Account Title and Explanation	Debit	Credit

e) Prepare the entry to pay the liability to the health insurance company on May 31, 2011:

Date	Account Title and Explanation	Debit	Credit

f) Prepare the entry to pay the liabilities to the government on June 15, 2011:

Date	Account Title and Explanation	Debit	Credit

Case Study

CS-1 (❻)

Tarantula Publishing prints advertising flyers, booklets and magazines for customers. The company employs 12 employees who work the small printing presses and binding machines. Susan is the bookkeeper and deals with all items relating to the financial recordkeeping of the business. Among her many duties, she prepares all the paperwork for new hires, collects the punch cards from the employees at the end of each pay period and completes and signs the paycheques.

When a new employee is hired, the general manager sends the individual to Susan to complete the appropriate paperwork for payroll. Susan is responsible for properly completing the paperwork regarding the employee's SIN, gross pay and other details.

Susan sometimes has to track down employees to get their time cards so she can pay them. Employees manually fill out the time cards and sometimes take them home in their uniforms.

The general manager does not review the paycheques that Susan writes. He is often too busy dealing with customers and planning the production runs to have time to do much of the paperwork that Susan presents him. Since Susan is allowed to sign cheques, she prepares the cheques and hands them out to the employees.

Susan prepares the paycheques manually and is currently using the 2010 payroll tables to calculate income tax, CPP and EI deductions. The 2011 year has just started, and Susan is unaware that the rates for income tax, CPP and EI change each year. She is still using the 2010 payroll tables for 2011 paycheques.

Required:

a) What are the consequences of using older payroll tables to calculate payroll deductions?

____

____

____

____

b) Discuss the control issues with this company and what can be done to implement better controls.

Chapter 11

THE CASH FLOW STATEMENT

Assessment Questions

AS-1 (❶)

Is the cash flow statement an optional statement? Explain.

____

____

AS-2 (❷)

Identify the three ways a business can generate and use cash.

____

____

AS-3 (❷)

What does cash flow from operations represent?

____

____

AS-4 (❷)

What does cash flow from investments represent?

____

____

AS-5 (❷)

What does cash flow from financing represent?

____

____

AS-6 (❸)

What financial statements are required to prepare a cash flow statement?

AS-7 (❸)

Which items appear in the cash flow from operations section of the cash flow statement?

AS-8 (❸)

Which items appear in the cash flow from investing section of the cash flow statement?

AS-9 (❸)

Which items appear in the cash flow from financing section of the cash flow statement?

AS-10 (❸)

What does a gain on the sale of equipment indicate?

AS-11 (❸)

How is a gain on the sale of equipment shown on the cash flow statement?

Application Questions

AP-1 (❶)

For each item listed, indicate how the item will impact cash flow (increase, decrease or no change) using the indirect method.

Item	Effect on Cash
Net Income	
Increase in Accounts Payable	
Decrease in Accounts Receivable	
Purchase of Property, Plant and Equipment	
Payment of Bank Loan	
Increase in Inventory	
Pay Dividends	
Increase in Shareholders' Loans	
Increase in Prepaid Insurance	

AP-2 (❷)

Indicate the section of the cash flow statement where each item would be located (operations, investing or financing).

Item	Section
Change in Accounts Payable	
Change in Inventory	
Change in Property, Plant and Equipment	
Change in Long-term portion of Bank Loan	
Change in Short-term portion of Bank Loan	
Change in Prepaid Rent	
Change in Accounts Receivable	
Change in Common Shares	
Gain on Sale of Property, Plant and Equipment	

AP-3 (❷)

The net income for the year ended on December 31, 2010 for RC Corporation was $120,000. Additional data for the year is provided below:

Purchase of fixed assets	$280,000
Depreciation of fixed assets	14,000
Dividends declared	50,000
Net decrease in accounts receivable	29,000
Loss on sale of equipment	13,000

Required:

Calculate the increase in cash from operating activities.

____

____

____

____

AP-4 (❷)

Bonus Company had the following amounts in its cash flow statement for the year ended December 31, 2011:

Net decrease in cash from operations	$100,000
Net decrease in cash from investment	400,000
Net increase in cash from financing	350,000
Cash balance, January 1, 2011	600,000

Required:

Calculate the cash balance at December 31, 2011.

____

____

____

____

AP-5 (❷)

The following information is taken from Bush Company for the fiscal year 2011:

Purchase of plant and equipment	$33,000
Sale of long-term investment	12,000
Increase in accounts payable	6,000
Repayment of bonds payable	15,000
Depreciation on plant assets	7,000

Required:

Calculate the increase (decrease) in cash from investing activities.

AP-6 (❷)

The net income for the year ended December 31, 2011 for the Kersley Company was $73,000. Additional information is as follows:

Interest expense on borrowing	$8,000
Increase in accounts receivable	10,000
Decrease in prepaid expense	3,000
Decrease in accounts payable	4,000
Dividends paid to common shareholders	14,000

Required:

Calculate the increase (decrease) in cash from operating activities.

AP-7 (❷)

The Grading Company's cash account decreased by $14,000 and its short-term investment account increased by $18,000. Cash increase from operations was $21,000. Net cash decrease from investments was $22,000.

Required:

Based on the above information, calculate the cash increase (or decrease) from financing.

____

____

____

____

AP-8 (❸)

Balance sheet accounts for Planet Inc. contain the following amounts at the end of 2010 and 2011:

Planet Inc. Balance Sheet As at December 31		
	2011	**2010**
Assets		
Current Assets		
Cash	$7,500	$5,000
Accounts Receivable	21,000	15,000
Prepaid Expenses	2,500	2,000
Inventory	37,000	28,000
Total Current Assets	68,000	50,000
Non-Current Assets		
Property Plant and Equipment	196,000	175,000
Less: Accumulated Depreciation	(41,000)	(32,000)
Total Non-Current Assets	155,000	143,000
Total Assets	**$223,000**	**$193,000**
Liabilities		
Current Liabilities	$33,000	$33,000
Long-term Liabilities	30,000	35,000
Total Liabilities	**63,000**	**68,000**
Shareholders' Equity		
Common Shares	75,000	60,000
Retained Earnings	85,000	65,000
Total Shareholders' Equity	**160,000**	**125,000**
Total Liabilities and Equity	**$223,000**	**$193,000**

Assume current liabilities include only items from operations (e.g., accounts payable, tax payable). Long-term liabilities include items from financing (e.g. bonds and other long-term liabilities).

Required:

Prepare the cash flow statement for 2011. Assume the net income for 2011 was $20,000.

Planet, Inc. **Cash Flow Statement** **For the Year Ended December 31, 2011**		

AP-9 (❸)

Flax Corporation's balance sheet accounts as of December 31, 2011 and 2010 are presented below:

Flax Corp. Balance Sheet As at December 31		
	2011	**2010**
Assets		
Current Assets		
Cash	$460,000	$300,000
Short-term Investments	600,000	-
Accounts Receivable	1,020,000	1,020,000
Inventory	1,360,000	1,200,000
Total Current Assets	3,440,000	2,520,000
Non-Current Assets		
Long-term Investments	400,000	800,000
Property, Plant and Equipment	3,100,000	2,500,000
Less: Accumulated Depreciation	(900,000)	(600,000)
Total Non-Current Assets	2,600,000	2,700,000
Total Assets	**$6,040,000**	**$5,220,000**
Liabilities		
Current Liabilities	$2,300,000	$2,000,000
Long-term Liabilities	800,000	700,000
Total Liabilities	**3,100,000**	**2,700,000**
Shareholders' Equity		
Common Shares	1,800,000	1,680,000
Retained Earnings	1,140,000	840,000
Total Shareholders' Equity	**2,940,000**	**2,520,000**
Total Liabilities and Equity	**$6,040,000**	**$5,220,000**

Assume current liabilities include only items from operations (e.g., accounts payable, tax payable). Long-term liabilities include items from financing (e.g. bonds and other long-term liabilities).

Required:

Prepare the cash flow statement for 2011. Assume the net income for 2011 was $300,000.

Flax Corp. **Cash Flow Statement** **For the Year Ended December 31, 2011**		

AP-10 (❶)

Ashe Inc. reported the following data for 2011:

Income Statement	
Net Income	$30,000
Depreciation	4,000
Balance Sheet	
Increase in Accounts Receivable	9,000
Decrease in Accounts Payable	7,000

Required:

Calculate the increase (decrease) in cash from operations.

AP-11 (❸)

Use the following information to prepare the operations section of a cash flow statement for MNO Co. for 2011:

Net income	$140,000
Increase in inventory	30,000
Increase in accounts payable	20,000
Depreciation expense	55,000
Increase in accounts receivable	18,000
Gain on sale of land	25,000

AP-12 (❸)

Breakwater Boats sells boating accessories. At the end of 2011, the income statement and comparative balance sheet were prepared as shown below. Based on the information given, prepare a cash flow statement for Breakwater Boats.

Breakwater Boats Balance Sheet As at December 31	2011	2010
ASSETS		
Current Assets		
Cash	$73,870	$62,500
Accounts receivable	94,800	87,500
Inventory	327,000	245,700
Prepaid expenses	14,500	14,500
Total Current Assets	510,170	410,200
Property, plant & equipment[(1)]	340,000	384,000
Less: Accumulated depreciation	(26,200)	(24,500)
TOTAL ASSETS	$823,970	$769,700
LIABILITIES AND EQUITY		
Liabilities		
Current Liabilities		
Accounts payable	$52,600	$45,700
Current portion of bank loan	8,500	8,500
Total Current Liabilities	61,100	54,200
Long-term portion of bank loan	50,100	58,600
TOTAL LIABILITIES	111,200	112,800
Shareholders' Equity		
Common shares	150,000	150,000
Retained earnings[(2)]	562,770	506,900
TOTAL SHAREHOLDERS' EQUITY	712,770	656,900
TOTAL LIABILITIES AND EQUITY	$823,970	$769,700

Additional Information:

1. Property, Plant & Equipment
   During 2011, equipment was sold for a gain of $6,000. The cash proceeds from the sale totalled $50,000.
2. Retained Earnings
   Breakwater Boats declared and paid $35,000 in dividends in 2011.

Breakwater Boats Income Statement For the Year Ended December 31, 2011	
Sales	$562,000
COGS	365,300
Gross Profit	196,700
Operating Expenses	
Depreciation Expense	1,700
Other Operating Expenses	61,200
Total Operating Expenses	62,900
Operating Income	133,800
Other Income	
Gain on Sale of Equipment	6,000
Net Income Before Tax	139,800
Income Tax	48,930
Net Income	$90,870

Required:

Create the cash flow statement.

Breakwater Boats Cash Flow Statement For the Year Ended December 31, 2011		

AP-13 (❸)

Vortex Manufacturing makes and sells integrated circuit boards. At the end of 2011, the income statement and comparative balance sheet were prepared as shown below. Based on the information given, prepare a cash flow statement for Vortex Manufacturing.

Vortex Manufacturing
Balance Sheet
As at December 31

	2011	2010
ASSETS		
Current Assets		
Cash	$239,820	$135,640
Accounts receivable	242,100	265,300
Inventory	503,200	465,300
Prepaid expenses	26,500	26,500
Total Current Assets	1,011,620	892,740
Property, plant & equipment[1]	840,400	856,400
Less: Accumulated depreciation	(102,300)	(95,600)
TOTAL ASSETS	$1,749,720	$1,653,540
LIABILITIES AND EQUITY		
Liabilities		
Current Liabilities		
Accounts payable	$305,600	$324,500
Current portion of bank loan	32,000	23,000
Total Current Liabilities	337,600	347,500
Long-term portion of bank loan	205,000	185,000
TOTAL LIABILITIES	542,600	532,500
Shareholders' Equity		
Common shares	290,000	260,000
Retained earnings[2]	917,120	861,040
TOTAL SHAREHOLDERS' EQUITY	1,207,120	1,121,040
TOTAL LIABILITIES AND EQUITY	$1,749,720	$1,653,540

Additional Information:

1. Property, Plant & Equipment
   During 2011, equipment was sold for a loss of $5,000. The cash proceeds from the sale totalled $11,000.
2. Retained Earnings
   Vortex Manufacturing declared and paid $50,000 in dividends in 2011.

Vortex Manufacturing **Income Statement** **For the Year Ended December 31, 2011**	
Sales	$2,650,000
COGS	1,722,500
Gross Profit	927,500
Operating Expenses	
Depreciation Expense	6,700
Other operating expenses	752,600
Total Operating Expenses	759,300
Operating Income	168,200
Other Income	
Loss on Sale of Equipment	(5,000)
Net Income Before Tax	163,200
Income Tax	57,120
Net Income	$106,080

Required:

Create the cash flow statement.

Vortex Manufacturing Cash Flow Statement For the Year Ended December 31, 2011		

Case Study

CS-1 (❸)

Granite Surfaces specializes in making granite countertops. A new accounting clerk has compiled the following information to prepare the cash flow statement for the year ended December 31, 2011.

- Net income for the year was $114,140.
- Depreciation expense was $15,300.
- Equipment was sold for a gain of $16,000. Cash proceeds from the sale were $36,000.
- Equipment was purchased for $250,000.
- Dividends of $50,000 were paid.
- Accounts receivable increased by $31,400.
- Inventory decreased by $38,700.
- Accounts payable increased by $41,100.
- Bank loans increased by $55,000.
- Shares were sold for $50,000 (also their book value).
- Cash balance on January 1, 2011 was $114,800.
- Cash balance on December 31, 2011 was $117,640.

The cash flow statement the accounting clerk prepared is shown below.

Granite Surfaces Cash Flow Statement For the Year Ended December 31, 2011		
Cash Flow from Operations		
Add: Net income	$114,140	
Add: Depreciation	15,300	
Changes in Current Assets & Current Liabilities:		
Increase in accounts receivable	31,400	
Decrease in inventory	(38,700)	
Increase in accounts payable	41,100	
Sale of equipment	36,000	
Purchase of equipment	(250,000)	
Change in Cash due to Operations		($50,760)
Cash Flow from Investments		
Receipt of bank loan	55,000	
Change in Cash due to Investments		55,000
Cash Flow from Financing		
Payment of cash dividend	(50,000)	
Sale of common shares	50,000	
Change in Cash due to Financing		0
Net increase (decrease) in cash		4,240
Cash at the beginning of the year		114,800
Cash at the end of the year		$119,040

Required:

1) Identify the problems with the cash flow statement that the accounting clerk prepared.

2) Prepare a corrected cash flow statement.

Granite Surfaces Cash Flow Statement For the Year Ended December 31, 2011		

Notes

Chapter 12

FINANCIAL STATEMENT ANALYSIS

Assessment Questions

AS-1 (❶)

What is financial analysis?

AS-2 (❷)

What is the formula for gross profit margin?

AS-3 (❷)

What does gross profit margin tell us?

AS-4 (❷)

What does EBITDA refer to?

AS-5 (❷)

What is the formula for the interest coverage ratio?

____

____

AS-6 (❷)

Is it more preferable to have a higher or lower interest coverage ratio? Explain.

____

____

AS-7 (❷)

How do you calculate net profit margin?

____

____

AS-8 (❷)

What is the formula for return on equity?

____

____

____

AS-9 (❷)

For a particular company, if net income increased significantly from one year to the next, does this guarantee that the return on equity will also increase? Explain.

____

____

____

AS-10 (❷)

How do you calculate return on assets?

AS-11 (❷)

What are some possible reasons why return on assets may have decreased from one period to the next?

AS-12 (❷)

Suppose that company A and company B generate the same level of net income each period. However, company A is more capital-intensive than company B. Which company will likely have the higher return on assets?

AS-13 (❸)

What is the formula for the current ratio?

AS-14 (❸)

What does the current ratio tell you?

AS-15 (❸)

If current assets stay constant from one period to the next, but current liabilities increases, what will happen to the current ratio?

____

____

AS-16 (❸)

What is the formula for the quick ratio?

____

____

AS-17 (❸)

How do you calculate the debt-to-equity ratio?

____

____

AS-18 (❹)

What is the formula for days-sales-outstanding?

____

____

AS-19 (❹)

What does days-sales-outstanding tell you?

____

____

AS-20 (❹)

How do you calculate accounts receivable turnover?

____

____

AS-21 (❹)

How is inventory days on hand calculated?

____

____

AS-22 (❹)

What is the formula for the inventory turnover ratio?

____

____

AS-23 (❶)

Define debt covenant.

____

____

____

Application Questions

AP-1 (❷)

A company reported the following:

- Sales: $1 million
- Cost of Goods Sold: $0.7 million
- Operating Expenses: $0.4 million
- Income Taxes: $0.2 million

Calculate the gross profit margin. Differentiate between gross profit margin and gross profit.

AP-2 (❷)

Gross profit increased from $0.3 million in 2009, to $0.4 million in 2010. Gross profit margin decreased from 30% in 2009, to 28% in 2010. Comment on whether or not the company's profitability improved or deteriorated.

AP-3 (❷)

A company reported the following:

Sales	$2.0 million
Cost of Goods Sold	0.7 million
Operating Expenses	0.4 million
Depreciation included in operating expenses	0.1 million
Interest expense included in operating expenses	0.05 million
Income taxes	40% of income before tax
Owners' Equity (Average)	$20.0 million

Required: Calculate the EBITDA

AP-4 (❷)

Use the information supplied in AP-3. Calculate the net profit margin.

AP-5 (❷)

Use the information supplied in AP-3. Calculate the interest coverage ratio.

AP-6 (❷)

Use the information supplied in AP-3. Calculate the return on equity. Banks are currently paying interest on deposits of 4% for money invested for 2 or more years. Comment on the ratio.

AP-7 (❸)

A company reports current assets of $6,572, and current liabilities of $2,786. Calculate the current ratio.

AP-8 (❸)

Total current liabilities for a company are $2,786. If cash is $2,000, short-term investments are $3,000, long-term investments are $1,000 and accounts receivable is $1,200, calculate the quick ratio.

AP-9 (❸)

A company had a debt to equity ratio last year of 1.46. This year, the ratio is 2.0. Are things getting better or worse? Explain your answer.

AP-10 (❹)

ABC Company sells on credit, with the balance due in 30 days. The company's DSO ratio has changed from 60 days last year to 42 days this year. Are things getting better or worse? Explain the relationship between the sales terms and DSO.

AP-11 (❹)

At the end of 2010, accounts receivable amounts to $210,000. At the beginning of the year it was $200,000. Net credit sales for the year amounted to $900,000 and net income was calculated to be $205,000.

Determine the days sales outstanding ratio and the accounts receivable turnover ratio.

AP-12 (❹)

At the beginning of 2009, Acatela Corp. had inventory of $350,000. During the year, they purchased $220,000 worth of raw materials and sold $500,000 worth of inventory. Determine the inventory turnover ratio and the inventory days on hand ratio.

AP-13 (❶)

Financial statement analysis is performed on historical information. Since the past can not be changed, calculating financial ratios is of no use. What management and investors are really interested in is the future, specifically the future profitability of a company. Discuss.

AP-14 (➊)

The income statement of Ellen Corporation for the years 2009 and 2010 showed the following gross profit.

	2010	2009
Sales Revenue	$97,200	$80,000
Cost of Goods Sold	72,000	50,000
Gross Profit	$25,200	$30,000

Required:

a) Calculate the gross profit margins for both years.

b) In which year does Ellen Corporation have a better gross profit margin? Explain.

AP-15 (➊)

Selected information for the Universal Company is as follows:

	December 31		
	2011	2010	2009
Common Shares	$840,000	$648,000	$550,000
Retained Earnings	370,000	248,000	150,000
Net income for the year	240,000	122,000	98,000

Required:

a) Calculate the return on equity ratio for 2011 and 2010.

b) Has The Universal Company's performance improved in 2011? Explain using the return on equity ratio.

AP-16 (❶)

Presented below is the comparative income statement of Newton Company for 2011 and 2010.

Newton Company Income Statement For the Year Ended December 31, 2011		
	2011	**2010**
Sales	$194,890	$108,345
Cost of Goods Sold	116,934	65,007
Gross Profit	77,956	43,338
Operating Expenses:		
Advertising	4,000	2,000
Bank Charges	580	0
Communication	5,380	3,684
Legal and Professional	6,000	3,950
Utilities	3,330	1,503
Rent Expense	3,500	3,500
Repairs and Maintenance	4,000	2,500
Salaries and Wages	3,000	1,800
Transportation	3,200	1,700
Interest	1,248	580
Depreciation	1,550	990
Total Operating Expenses	35,788	22,207
Operating Profit before tax	42,168	21,131
Income Tax	12,650	6,339
Net Profit	**$29,518**	**$14,792**

Required:

a) Calculate the following ratios for both years:

- EBITDA Percentage to Sales
- Interest Coverage Ratio

b) In which year does the company have a better performance with respect to the ratios calculated in part a)? Explain.

____

____

____

____

AP-17 (❷)

Selected financial data from Crew Company is provided below:

	As at December 31, 2010
Cash	$75,000
Accounts Receivable	225,000
Merchandise Inventory	270,000
Short-Term Investments	40,000
Land and Building	500,000
Current Portion of Long-Term Debt	30,000
Accounts Payable	120,000

Required:

a) Calculate the quick ratio.

____

____

____

____

____

____

b) What does Crew Company's quick ratio suggest about the company's performance?

____

____

AP-18 (❷)

Information from Silky Company's year-end financial statements is as follows:

	2010	2009
Current Assets	$200,000	$210,000
Current Liabilities	100,000	90,000
Shareholders' Equity	250,000	270,000
Net Sales	830,000	880,000
Cost of Goods Sold	620,000	640,000
Operating Income	50,000	55,000

Required:

a) Calculate the current ratio for both years.

b) In which year does Silky Company have a better current ratio? Explain.

Case Study

CS-1(❶, ❷, ❸, ❹)

Suppose that you have decided to invest some money in the stock market. After some research online, you come across the financial statements of Research in Motion. Before you can make a decision to invest in the company, you will need to calculate some key financial ratios and then analyze them. The statements are presented below.

Research in Motion **Consolidated Balance Sheet (in thousands)** **As at February 28, 2010 and February 28, 2009**		
	Feb 2010	**Feb 2009**
Assets		
Cash	1,550,861	835,546
Short-term Investments	360,614	682,666
Accounts Receivable	2,800,115	2,269,845
Inventory	621,611	682,400
Other Current Assets	479,455	371,129
Total Current Assets	**5,812,656**	**4,841,586**
Long-Term Investment	958,248	720,635
Fixed Assets, net	1,956,581	1,334,648
Intangible Assets	1,476,924	1,204,503
Total Assets	**$10,204,409**	**$8,101,372**
Liabilities		
Accounts Payable	$615,620	$448,339
Accrued Liabilities	1,638,260	1,238,602
Income Taxes Payable	95,650	361,460
Other Current Liabilities	82,247	66,950
Total Current Liabilities	**2,431,777**	**2,115,351**
Long-term Liabilities	169,969	111,893
Total Liabilities	**2,601,746**	**2,227,244**
Shareholders' Equity		
Common Shares	2,113,146	2,208,235
Retained Earnings	5,489,517	3,665,893
Shareholders' Equity	**7,602,663**	**5,874,128**
Liabilities + Shareholders' Equity	**$10,204,409**	**$8,101,372**

Research in Motion Consolidated Income Statement (in thousands) For the Year Ended February 28, 2010 and February 28, 2009		
	Feb 2010	**Feb 2009**
Revenue	$14,953,224	$11,065,186
Cost of Sales	8,368,958	5,967,888
Gross Profit	6,584,266	5,097,298
Operating expenses		
Research and Development	964,841	684,702
Selling, Marketing and Admin	1,907,398	1,495,697
Amortization	310,357	194,803
Litigation	163,800	0
Total Expenses	3,346,396	2,375,202
Operating Income Before Tax	**3,237,870**	**2,722,096**
Investment Income	28,640	78,267
Income Before Income Tax	3,266,510	2,800,363
Income Tax Expense	809,366	907,747
Net Income	**$2,457,144**	**$1,892,616**

Research in Motion Summary of the Cash Flow Statement (in thousands) For the Year Ended February 28, 2010 and February 28, 2009		
	Feb 2010	**Feb 2009**
Net Cash Provided by Operations	$3,034,874	$1,451,845
Net Cash Used by Investing	($1,470,127)	($1,823,523)
Net Cash Used by Financing	($849,432)	$22,826
Net Increase (Decrease) in Cash	**$715,315**	**($348,852)**

Required:

a) Calculate the following ratios for Research in Motion for 2010 and 2009. For any ratios that require an average (i.e. ROE), use the closing balance for the year.

	2010	**2009**
Gross Profit Margin		
EBITDA		
EBITDA Percentage to Sales		
Net Profit Margin		
Return on Equity		
Return on Assets		
Asset Turnover		
Current Ratio		
Quick Ratio		
Debt-to-Equity Ratio		

b) Based on the figures you calculated, has the company shown improvement in 2010 over 2009? Would you invest in Research in Motion? Explain.

CS-2 (❶, ❷, ❸, ❹)

The following information has been taken from the financial statements of Ivory Inc.

Ivory Inc.	
Current Assets, December 31, 2010	175,000
Total Assets, January 1, 2010	500,000
Total Assets, December 31, 2010	575,000
Current Liabilities, December 31, 2010	75,000
Total Liabilities, December 31, 2010	175,000
Shareholders' Equity, January 1, 2010	300,000
Shareholders' Equity, December 31, 2010	400,000
Net Sales	900,000
Depreciation	10,000
Interest Expense	20,000
Income Tax Expense	25,000
Net Income	40,000

a) Given the above data for Ivory Inc., calculate the following ratios for 2010 (round to two decimal places). The company's ratios for 2009 are given for comparison.

	Ratio	2009
i)	Current Ratio	3.5
ii)	Interest Coverage Ratio	5.40
iii)	Debt to Equity	25.00%
iv)	Return on Assets	12.50%
v)	Return on Equity	20.20%
vi)	Net Profit Margin	8.60%

b) Using 2009 as a comparison, discuss whether the company improved or deteriorated in its ability to (i) pay current liabilities as they come due, (ii) meet its long-term debt obligations and (iii) profitability. Be sure to make reference to specific ratios in your answers.

Your Answer:

a)

	Ratio	2010	2009
i)			
ii)			
iii)			
iv)			
v)			
vi)			

Chapter 13

BUDGETS

Assessment Questions

AS-1 (❶)

What is a budget?

AS- 2 (❶)

Describe a benefit of budgeting.

AS- 3 (❶)

What is a cash budget?

AS- 4 (❷)

What is involved in the planning stage of the budgeting process?

AS- 5 (❷)

What is involved in the controlling stage of the budgeting process?

AS- 6 (❸)

Briefly describe incremental budgeting.

AS- 7 (❸)

What is one advantage of using the incremental budgeting approach?

AS- 8 (❸)

What is one disadvantage of using the incremental budgeting approach?

AS- 9 (❸)

Briefly describe zero-based budgeting.

AS- 10 (❹)

What is top-down budgeting?

AS- 11 (❹)

What is bottom-up budgeting?

AS- 12 (❺)

Define budgetary slack.

AS- 13 (❺)

If an organization has budgetary slack, how does it affect the company?

AS- 14 (❼)

What does a variance report show?

AS- 15 (❼)

If budgeted sales were greater than actual sales, is this variance favourable or unfavourable? Explain.

AS- 16 (❼)

If budgeted costs were greater than actual costs, is this variance favourable or unfavourable? Explain.

AS- 17 (❽)

List two tips to remember when building a budget.

AS- 18 (❽)

List two key tips to remember when creating a departmental budget "bottom-up."

Application Questions

AP-1 (❽)

For the upcoming year, Kinston Quart Limited expects to generate $4,000,000 of revenue. Based on historical trends, the company makes the most sales in the first two quarters. As a result, it assumes that the first and second quarter will each contribute 30% of the annual revenue. The remaining budgeted amount will be allocated equally between the last two quarters.

Required:

For each quarter, calculate the budgeted sales in dollars.

___

___

___

___

AP-2 (❽)

Amanda Henderson is getting ready for her first year in university. In order to get funding from her parents, she is required to prepare a cash budget for the first semester.

Expected Expenditures:	
Tuition fees due on September 20	$2,500
Rent due at the beginning of each month	500
Food per month	265
Entertainment per month	110
Expected Income:	
Part-time job: Monthly wage	$370

Required:

For each month of the first semester (i.e. September, October, November and December), determine the amount of money that Amanda's parents should give her. Classes and rent start on September 1st. Assume that Amanda spends the same amount of money on food and entertainment every month.

AP-3 (❸)

The following is Alpha Hardware Corporation's income statement for the year ended December 31, 2010:

Alpha Hardware Corporation **Income Statement** **For the Year Ended December 31, 2010**	
Revenues	$800,000
Cost of Goods Sold	480,000
Gross Profit	320,000
Operating Expenses:	
Administrative Costs	25,000
Selling Costs	18,000
Salaries	95,000*
Rent	25,000
Total Operating Expenses	163,000
Net Income	$157,000

*Comprised of $65,000 in managers' salaries and $30,000 in office employees' salaries

Alpha Hardware is a small business and it does not intend to spend a lot of time and money on budgeting. The manager has determined the 2011 budgeted income statement should simply reflect the following predicted changes from the 2010 income statement:

- Revenues will increase by 2.5%
- Gross profit will increase by 5%
- Selling costs will decrease by 3%
- Managers' salaries will increase by 8%
- Administrative costs, office employees' salaries, and rent expense will remain the same

Required:

Prepare the budgeted income statement for the year ending December 31, 2011 using the incremental budgeting approach.

Alpha Hardware Corporation Budgeted Income Statement For the Year Ending December 31, 2011	

AP-4 (❸)

The following is Gauss Appliance Corporation's income statement for the year ended April 30, 2011:

Gauss Appliance Corporation Income Statement For the Year Ended April 30, 2011	
Revenue	$400,000
Cost of Goods Sold	$220,000
Gross Profit	180,000
Operating Expenses:	
Administrative Expense	30,000
Maintenance Expense	14,000
Salaries Expense	70,000
Rent Expense	20,000
Total Operating Expenses	134,000
Net Income	$46,000

Gauss Appliance is a small business and it does not intend to spend a lot of time and money on budgeting. The manager has determined the 2012 budgeted income statement should simply reflect the following predicted changes from the 2011 income statement:

- Revenue will increase by 4%
- Gross profit will increase by 2%
- Maintenance expense will increase by 1.5%
- Salaries expense will decrease by 3%
- Administrative costs and rent expense will remain the same

Required:

Prepare the budgeted income statement for the year ending April 30, 2012 using the incremental budgeting approach.

Gauss Appliance Corporation Budgeted Income Statement For the Year Ending April 30, 2012	

AP-5 (❷, ❸, ❹, ❺)

Match the following terms with the descriptions provided in the table below.

- Planning
- Controlling
- Incremental budgeting
- Zero-based budgeting
- Top-down budgeting
- Bottom-up budgeting
- Budgetary slack

Term (fill in):	Description:
	This occurs when budgeted expenses are intentionally overestimated
	A stage in the budgeting process where actual results are compared to the budget
	A budgeting approach which requires the creation of budgets from scratch
	Also known as imposed budgeting
	A budgeting method where managers of all levels fully co-operate
	An approach to budgeting that requires dependence on the previous period's budget
	A stage in the budgeting process where budgets are created to meet short-term objectives

AP-6 (❻)

Suppose that a company budgeted that total sales for a period would amount to $910,000. The company also budgeted cost of goods sold to be $620,000. Actual sales for the period totalled $840,000 and actual cost of goods sold was $590,000.

Required:

a) What is the variance in total sales? Is it favourable or unfavourable?

____

____

____

b) What is the variance in cost of goods sold? Is it favourable or unfavourable?

____

____

____

AP-7 (❻)

Suppose that a company budgeted that total sales for a period would amount to $300,000. The company also budgeted gross profit to be $160,000. Actual sales for the period totalled $350,000 and actual gross profit was $160,000.

Required:

a) What is the variance in total sales? Is it favourable or unfavourable?

____

____

____

b) What is the variance in cost of goods sold? Is it favourable or unfavourable?

AP-8 (❺)

Suppose that a company is in the process of creating the budgeted income statement. Consider budgeted maintenance expense. Assume that a reasonable estimate for maintenance expense for the budgeted period is $14,000. However, the company actually included an estimate of $18,000 for maintenance expense on the budgeted income statement. Did the company create any budgetary slack with respect to maintenance expense? If so, what is the amount of the budgetary slack?

AP-9 (❺)

Suppose that a company is in the process of creating the budgeted income statement. Consider budgeted revenue. Assume that a reasonable estimate for revenue for the budgeted period is $600,000. However, the company actually included an estimate of $650,000 for revenue on the budgeted income statement. Did the company create any budgetary slack with respect to budgeted revenue? If so, what is the amount of the budgetary slack?

AP-10 (❼)

Layton Bakery created the sales budget (shown below) for the year ending November 30, 2010. The sales are broken down by each quarter of the year.

Layton Bakery Budgeted Sales Report (by Quarter) For the Year Ending November 30, 2010	
Quarter 1 Sales	$125,000
Quarter 2 Sales	156,000
Quarter 3 Sales	98,000
Quarter 4 Sales	78,000
Total Sales	$457,000

The actual sales report for the year is shown below.

Layton Bakery Sales Report (by Quarter) For the Year Ended November 30, 2010	
Quarter 1 Sales	$150,000
Quarter 2 Sales	152,000
Quarter 3 Sales	76,000
Quarter 4 Sales	42,000
Total Sales	$420,000

Required:

Prepare a sales variance report for 2010.

Layton Bakery Sales Variance Report For the Year Ended November 30, 2010

AP-11 (❻, ❼)

Max Braggins Company created the following budgeted income statement for the year ending December 31, 2010:

Max Braggins Company Budgeted Income Statement For the Year Ending December 31, 2010	
Revenue	$555,000
Cost of Goods Sold	350,000
Gross Profit	205,000
Operating Expenses	
Supplies	4,000
Accounting and professional services	6,000
Administration salaries	8,000
Advertising	14,000
Depreciation	12,000
Rent & utilities	75,000
Sales salaries	61,000
Total Operating Expenses	180,000
Net Income	$25,000

The actual income statement for the year is shown below.

Max Braggins Company Income Statement For the Year Ended December 31, 2010	
Revenue	$480,000
Cost of Goods Sold	300,000
Gross Profit	180,000
Operating Expenses	
Supplies	4,000
Accounting and professional services	6,000
Administration salaries	10,000
Advertising	9,000
Depreciation	11,000
Rent & utilities	80,000
Sales salaries	71,000
Total Operating Expenses	191,000
Net Income	$(11,000)

Required:

Prepare an income statement variance report for 2010.

Max Braggins Company Income Statement Variance Report For the Year Ended December 31, 2010

Case Study

CS-1 (❶, ❸, ❹, ❺, ❽)

Tom Ato is the President and CEO of a popular chain restaurant-lounge which serves local organic vegetarian dishes throughout the United States. Every year, Tom meets with upper management of Tomayto Restaurant Group at head office, along with his team of accountants in order to establish a budget for the following year. This budget is then rolled out throughout the organization to the separate departments. The departments include: sales and marketing, human resources, accounting and finance, purchasing, and restaurant management.

Recently, Tom has noticed some problems with the effectiveness of his budgets and has hired you, a financial advisor, to help him improve his system.

The budgeting process has always been troublesome for Tom. The departments are very hostile towards each other regarding who gets a stricter budget each year. Lower management does not have any say regarding the budget.

A few years ago, Tom introduced a new incentive program where every manager who was able meet the budget was awarded a bonus based on how much money they saved. Tom always liked to save more because he knows that restaurants are particularly vulnerable in an economic downturn, and he wants to make sure Tomayto survives. He always emphasizes cost savings and managers who were not able to meet the budget do not receive great performance reviews.

When this program was first introduced, he found that many managers were unable to meet the budgeted figures, calling them "unfair" and "impossible". Although the recent business environment has changed drastically, Tomayto still uses a system of incremental budgeting where figures in the budgets are based on prior year's spendings. Over time, the budget has been increased significantly. At the same time, Tom noticed that managers are able to not only meet the figures, but tend to spend exactly the amount of budgeted expenses. He finds this quite odd and has asked you to suggest the reason as to why it could be happening.

At the end of the year 2010, the company started a new line of restaurants under the name of Potayto. The Potayto project was not accounted for in the budgets for 2010. The Potayto project required working capital of $900,000 upfront to get started. However, Tom realized that he is unable to finance this amount through the cash from the company's accounts. He finds this odd because the company estimated $4,000,000 in net income for 2010. The balance of the cash account at the end of 2009 was $300,000. Note that $5,000,000 was spent in 2010 buying new property for many of the restaurant's stores. Tom wants you to give him a possible reason for why he does not have enough cash on hand despite the large projected net income figure.

Required:

1. Address Tom Ato's concerns and highlight some major issues in his budgeting process.
2. Give some suggestions for how Tomayto Restaurant Group's budgetary control system can be made more effective.